BEFORE THE EARTH DEVOURS US

Before the Earth Devours Us

Esteban Rodríguez

Published by Split/Lip Press
6710 S. 87th St.
Ralston, NE 68127
www.splitlippress.com

ISBN: 978-1-952897-19-1

Cover Design by David Wojciechowski

Editing by Lauren Westerfield

Contents

"I suppose if you're scared enough, you're capable of doing anything."

—Tomás Rivera, *...y no se lo tragó la tierra*

AFTER THE PYRE

I wanted to kill my stepfather. I'd dream it. Daydream it. Imagine myself standing over him in the middle of a field, watching blood spurt from the puncture wound on his chest—his white wife beater quickly turning red. I'd picture his cracked, inebriated lips struggling for breath, stammering a string of syllables that sounded like *Why*, ¿Por *qué?*, while I—clenching the gun or knife tighter in my hand—searched for an answer that would not only add a sense of closure, but would remind him that his life had always been beyond the boundaries of redemption.

Santos lived with his mother across the street from us. From what I knew, his mother was dying, had been for years: old age, diabetes, new bouts of what I could now guess was bronchitis, pneumonia, or some chronic strain of the flu that required weekly visits from a home-health nurse, further fueling her unwillingness to continue being spoon-fed, sponge-bathed, diaper-changed, spoken to like a child, and taken to la pulga once—perhaps twice if she was feeling up to it—a month, where she was wheelchaired through the labyrinth of veteran vendors who studied the nightgowned skeleton she had become.

Though it's easy to picture her face—the strands of static-colored hair cascading over her forehead, temples, ears; the wrinkles and papier-mâché-like roughness of her cheeks—I'd only ever see her those afternoons when I'd sit on the porch steps and watch Santos carry her down the makeshift ramp my mother told me he had built, tilting her carefully through the sun-warped planks, pivoting when they reached the bottom, and then pushing her along the walkway of sunken, octagon-shaped bricks crookedly leading to the chain-link gate. "Don't stare," I can still hear my mother saying. "You should know better. It's rude to stare." But whenever I did stare at Santos and his mother, she was already walking over to help, to open the side of his or our van.

I should have been envious. I should have been committing myself to those predictable outbursts boys my age—give or take a few years—were known for when their fathers had left them early enough to retain only fragments of the moments they shared. I should have been that son sitting silently at the table, forking a plateful of spaghetti as protest for his stepfather's presence, answering *Alright, Okay, Good* when his mother asked him how his day was at school. I should have been watching him with contempt, molding an Oedipal mindset reserved exclusively for stepfathers, while trying to figure out what this—this hand touching, this waist grabbing, this ear whispering, this hand in my mother's back pocket—all meant. And although I can now include references as overused as Oedipus to help explain how it felt as though I were fulfilling some preordained prophecy every time I imagined myself standing over his dead or dying body, there was never any chance for me to embody an image of that son when our dinners together were merely outings at McDonald's or Golden Corral.

"¿Por qué no?" I remember him asking my grandmother one Saturday afternoon, the palms of his hands tapping the barbed ends of the chain-link fence that extended from my grandparents' house to ours. It was spring. The clouds were emaciated as always in south Texas, and despite the red and green blots on TV predicting a chance of scattered showers, the weather remained purgatorial.

"Sólo quiero hablar con ella. Sólo quiero ver a mi hija," he told my grandmother. My Spanish was still in its infancy, and even if two decades later at the age of 27 the double r's, diphthongs, and adjectives placed after nouns still feel foreign on my tongue, I know what Santos was pleading for that day. I knew that his flaring hand gestures meant he wanted to see my half-sister, cradle the baby she was in his arms, and be the father he expected himself to be, at least before he proceeded to corner my mother and curse her out, explain what a bitch, whore, backstabbing woman she had become in a language I didn't need to understand to see.

"Porque no," reiterated my grandmother. "No quiere hablar contigo. Ya. Nunca."

"But that's not right, Teresa. She's my daughter, too," he protested, pointing at my grandparents' house. I didn't know how he knew we were inside, but he knew, and he pointed, and he stood behind that fence trying to reason with my grandmother, waving his arms.

He had the body of a construction worker, of a man who put in twelve-hour shifts six days out of the week; whose flesh emanated the faint scent of wet cement; and whose hands—his right one missing the pinky, ring, and middle finger—appeared to be well acquainted with decades of second-hand tools, wood, concrete, and with the ins and outs of a trade every man in his family had, at some point in their lives, entered into.

Despite his wife beaters and white tees, his oil-stained Wranglers sagging from his waist, and his sole-worn steel toes with the hem of each pant leg tucked inside, he didn't work in construction, never had. From what I asked and learned from my mother during a phone call we had regarding his life, many years later, he had been out of work for more than half a decade because of a burn injury he suffered when a bomb exploded at a gas station in Florida, disfiguring and scarring 45% of his body, so that every time I looked at him, I'd think of Liam Neeson in *Darkman*, minus the embarrassment to go out in public, or the sense that he needed to bring the world to justice. He told my mother it was a small bomb a former, disgruntled employee had placed in the trash bins by the side of the store. One second he was walking out the front doors, the next he was rolling on the concrete—the lot, patrons, fire and smoke all blurring into one.

Of course, it was difficult to believe this narrative, to imagine a homemade bomb being planted at a gas station in the late-80s in Florida, to see him as a victim, a headline, a medically induced, comatose patient that despite years of skin grafts, would never look like himself again. Bombs were meant for movies. Bombs were meant for political retaliation, domestic terrorism, warzones in the Balkans or the Middle East, places whose mere names evoked thoughts of civil unrest, or for pictures in history textbooks with captions that described how night after night of them, reigning in clusters, destroyed a city, turned the landscape into ash and rubble. Bombs were not meant for Florida gas stations. They were not meant for my stepfather. They were not meant to be believable.

After hanging up, I felt the urge to investigate, learn how many people were wounded, how many dead, what the punishment for the bomber was, if he was ever caught. A simple internet search could have yielded news reports of a bombing or bombing-like incident within the past 20 years in Florida. But when I sat down and opened my laptop, typed the words *Florida* and *bomb*, I found myself quickly deleting the search. Who was I to challenge the story he told my mother? To undermine the claims she felt so inclined to believe?

Even as my voice grew skeptical when I uttered, "A bomb? What do you mean 'a bomb'?", my mother didn't hesitate in reiterating her initial response.

"It was a bomb. A small one. How do you think he got all those burns? Don't you remember the right side of his body? His arms? Remember he didn't have three fingers? That's why he had long hair, so it could cover his neck. It kept the sun from burning him up."

Perhaps at one point she, too, had experienced doubt about his story, had felt that he was merely stretching his account in order to impress her, show that in spite of the explosion—the car shrapnel, the distance he flew, the burns that enveloped his body—he was still alive, a testimony to some higher plan in which he had been included.

"No quiere. Ya te dije," said my grandmother, shaking her head. "Déjala en paz."

"Teresa, por favor," he said. "I just want to see Iris. Es todo. Nada más, señora. I just want to see her." He moved his hand up to his neck and with his index finger and thumb began scratching crab-like at his jaw.

I watched this from the half-opened window, my face nearly touching the mesh. My mother was in the kitchen talking to her twin brothers, Jaime and Javi. I could hear their voices. I could sense her urgency. I turned around and saw three silhouettes shifting back and forth. My sister, barely a year old, was in a baby rocker somewhere, but she wasn't crying, wasn't reflecting the mood that would have helped nudge the plotline along, guide us into a climax. No, she was the reason this was occurring and she was cast offstage, not even an audience member.

Jaime and Javi were in their teens, still a year or two away from graduating high school. They were thinner then, had fades and mustaches and wore long shirts, cheap silver chains, and baggy black jeans with the belts buckled just above their crotches. They walked as though they were part of a gang scoping out new neighborhood territory to claim. But their vice was cars, cars that formed a small collection along the border of the empty lot next to my grandmother's house; cars they worked on after school or on the weekends, adding hydraulics, swapping out the rims, gluing square or rectangular pieces of mirrors—which they themselves had measured and cut—along the dashboard and door, installing a chain steering wheel, or a black convertible top, or a new radio, or a pair of subwoofers that made my neck tingle every time they got me to sit in the backseat to listen to how 'badass' the bass sounded. With money I could only guess my grandparents lent them, they'd buy cars from friends and shady dealers, then take them to shadier shops that repainted them the way lowriders were supposed to be painted, designing the hood with a tiger, a lion, a wolf, or some striped, feral animal that could only be tamed by a half-naked, green-eyed warrior woman I'd always make the mistake of staring at too long.

My uncles thought of themselves not as mechanics or body shop experts, but as artists, and that's what they were when they were slouched over their incomplete canvases. But as they left my mother in the kitchen, moved out of their silhouettes, their faces—I remember—weren't the faces of teenage boys contemplating creative projects. Jaime opened the screen door. Javi trailed close behind.

My grandmother turned around. She knew what this was about. Had my grandfather not been confined to the bedroom in the back of the house, where he had been living horizontally for three or four years, nearly blind and immobile, getting up only to sit in the beige, sunken La-Z-Boy in the living room, he would have been out there in the yard, talking Santos down, convincing him to accept my mother's unwillingness to negotiate the terms of his involvement.

My grandmother took a step back, her gaze lying somewhere between shocked and expected. "Jaime, ¿qué haces?" she asked.

"The fuck man?" yelled Jaime.

"What the hell do you want?" joined Javi.

"She doesn't want to deal with you. Get the fuck out of here!"

"This has nothing to do with you, Javi," said Santos.

"It's Jaime, maricon."

"Sorry, sorry," said Santos, backing away from the fence. He raised his hands to his chest, looked down in what appeared to be a quick surrender, and then looked up the way a man looks up when they realize they cannot sacrifice any more ground than they've already given.

"Jaime, por favor," urged my grandmother. Jamie took a few steps forward, ignoring my grandmother's pleas. Though she yelled for them to stop, she also began moving toward the porch, not because she wanted to avoid the chaos, but because she wanted her sons to carry out some sibling duty that required them to protect their older sister the way she protected them, even if—despite their fifteen-year age difference—all my mother had done in the past was lessen the trouble they got into around the house.

Santos leaned back and with his crab hand attempted to make his case. "Jaime, I was just telling your mother here que all I want to do is see Maria Elena and Iris. And Esteban if he's there, too."

"She don't want to see you. Stop bothering her."

"You're gonna get your fucking ass kicked," said Javi.

"Look, look. That's between your sister and me," said Santos, snapping his crab hand across the air. "Iris is almost a year old and she won't let me see her. Think about it. I don't get to see my daughter for a year. A year. Do you think that's fair? She didn't want to tell me. That's not right."

No one wanted to hear about fairness that day, and even though I'd later try to sympathize with the fact that my mother had been a few months pregnant with my sister before she had decided to tell Santos about it, and that he had, in some sense, been deprived of what also belonged to him, I could never let myself feel guilty for things he himself should have been more responsible for.

As it was in this moment, however, my mother and Santos were already separated, and her decision to leave him, as she later told me, came when she found a Ziploc bag full of marijuana in the console of her van, stashed, carelessly, beneath insurance papers, old receipts, and cassette tapes. Though he resisted the divorce, maintained that he was merely holding the bag for a friend and had no intention of smoking or selling it, my mother made him leave the house. "I couldn't run the risk. I just couldn't," she said. "He was already drinking a lot and he had lied and if I got caught I would've lost both you and my job with the state. I had had it with him. So I kicked him out."

"He had it in the console?" I asked.

"Yes, and he specifically told me that he didn't. So no. When I found it, I didn't want anything more to do with him." There was a pause on my end, hinting at my disbelief about the situation. Marijuana, however, was easier to accept than a bomb.

"I didn't know that," I said. "I remember certain episodes, but not everything."

"Yes. That's what happened. He wasn't always bad. He had his good moments, don't get me wrong. This one time, we had no money. We were down to I think five or six dollars and we went to the corner store and you got off with him and you said you wanted a chocolate milk and he bought it for you. He wanted to buy a beer or something, I don't know. But he got you the milk instead and you were happy."

"That was nice," I said, trying to picture my three- or four-year-old self in the store with him, walking toward the freezers in the back. "It's hard to recall a lot of things," I said. "The moment that does stand out was when Jaime and Javi started fighting with him in grandma's front yard."

"Yeah," said my mother. "I told them to do it."

"You did? Why?" I asked, feeling as though I were coming to Santos' defense.

"Because he wouldn't leave me alone and I had had enough. He was always bothering us, and I just didn't want nothing to do with him no more."

"And they did it just like that?"

"Yes. They knew what was happening. They saw all the bruises and marks on me, and that's why they agreed. And I have no regrets about what they did. Why are you asking about all of this? You've never been interested in him before. Are you writing something?"

"No," I lied. "Just got curious. That's all."

In the front yard that afternoon, I recall my grandmother dressed in what looked like a nightgown. She wore brown huaraches. She wore her hair in a bun. She wore a curious and concerned look on her clay-colored face. She shouted, "Javi! Jaime! Por favor. No quiero que hagan nada." And there were my uncles shouting at Santos in Spanish, calling him "Maricon," "Puto," "Pinche güey quemado," "Pinche güey que no tiene verga," and sprinkling what I thought was the more intimidating English, the "Get the fuck off our property," the "Fucking leave you fucking asshole," the "You're fucking deaf or what?" And there was Santos, unable to verbally respond to their comments, and physically unwilling to either, overcome more by his impulse to show that he was a man by all accounts, that he did indeed have a dick, a verga.

Santos moved around the fence, rolling his shoulders back, popping his neck. He was tall, lanky, clumsy with every step, and whatever toughness his body claimed lied more in the fact that when you faced him you were facing a man who had already endured the beating of fire on his skin.

"Ya! The hell with you all. I'm gonna show you who you're messing with." He grabbed the end of the fence, where the gate should have been, and swung around. My grandmother moved closer to the porch as I moved forward, uncertain why I felt drawn to the way Javi took off his shirt—revealing a wife beater that did little to cover the dreamcatcher tattoo I had sworn not to mention to either my mother or grandmother—or why I admired the way Jaime began lifting his jeans and squatting low enough to parody a karate stance.

Javi took a few quick steps to his right, causing Santos to hesitate. He looked at Jaime, then at Javi, unsure who he should go after first. He settled for Javi, the closest, and as he moved toward him, Jaime lowered his head and charged at Santos, swinging his fists into a series of hooks that struck him in the ribs. Santos swung, hitting Jaime on the back of his head, hitting Javi's raised forearms partially protecting his face. But his punches weren't enough to stop Javi from gripping him by his shirt collar and pulling him down. Santos tripped on Javi's leg. He hit the ground and rolled to his side, looking up just in time to see Javi lunging, hitting him twice: once in the jaw, the other between his shoulder and chest. Jaime turned around, lifted his jeans again, and as Santos attempted to grab Javi by the arms, to keep him from landing any more hits, Jaime swung his right leg and kicked him in the thigh, hips, ribs.

These were my uncles. This was the same Jaime who, when I was in second grade, would pick me up after school one afternoon with his baby blue lowrider, becoming the center of discussion amongst my friends the next day; that half-disbelief, half-astonishment that I was related to the man inside that car, that I got to ride in the front seat with the windows down, the hydraulics slightly raised, the bass from some rap song spilling onto the pick-up lane. This was the same uncle I recall telling me to shut up if I didn't know the lyrics to a song, because mumbling shit I didn't know ruined the entire flow; a statement reiterated by Javi when, after challenging me to wrestle on my bed once, to show him what I was all about, pinned me to the pillow with his forearm across the nape of my neck, and repeatedly asked if I was going to continue slurring lyrics, interrupting his listening experience every time he invited me for a drive around the block.

Yes, this was Javi, my favorite of the two, the one I would later yell *fuck you* to when once, after waiting my turn for the piñata at my cousin Johnny's birthday party, he'd come up with the idea to blindfold all of his nieces and nephews, starting with me. I protested. I said it wasn't fair. I swung. I swung. And after a minute of missing that purple Ninja Turtle I so desperately wanted, needed to hit, I was told my turn was up, that I wouldn't get another chance. So I cried, ran to the nearest picnic table, buried my head in my arms and raised it only to yell my fated words when I heard Javi laughing, making jokes about me with a group of blurry, tear-distorted family members seated around him.

These were the uncles I would sleep over with on Saturday nights, drawing velociraptors, T-Rexes, and invented creatures on lined sheets of paper, and waking up in the morning to go to church not because I wanted to be faithful, but just so I could sit between them, feel like they were brothers.

Santos fell and rolled onto his stomach. His legs began jerking, as though he were trying to swim away. Javi punched harder, unconcerned that all he was hitting were the soles of Santos' boots. Santos got to his knees and crawled toward the driveway. Jaime landed two or three more kicks to his stomach, ribs. Santos plopped on the ground, then got to his feet. But before he could turn around, Jaime lunged in front and shoved him back down. After every kick, my uncles took a few steps back for a better start, like punters, like soccer players, like men who felt confident in the force they knew their legs were capable of. Though I wasn't sure why, they looked graceful, beautiful even if I ignored their sweat, their grunts, the desire in their faces that shuddered them out of focus, made it appear as though all of this was happening in slow motion.

I remembered feeling myself moving at that same pace when I kneeled behind my grandmother's white van early one morning. It was summer. My mother was at work. My grandmother was picking lemons in the backyard, piling them into a large bowl, while my grandfather was in his room, still sleeping, still dying, still clinging to I wasn't sure what. I was supposed to be watching TV, entertaining myself with the *Price is Right*. But I was outside, breaking the lowest hanging branches from the trees in my grandmother's garden, stacking them inside my shirttail, and one by one stuffing each into the van's muffler. I had seen my mother crying. I had seen Santos grab her by the forearm, leaving pink and purplish marks. I wanted to kill him. In my mind my plan was flawless, all it needed was execution, a steady hand, a willingness to stuff as many sticks into my grandmother's muffler as I could fit, because I was convinced that when she reversed and took off down the street, the branches, unable to commit to tight spaces, would backfire and shoot out like bullets at Santos' house. I had no idea if Santos would be outside at the exact time my grandmother went out and ran errands, but if he was, if he was lingering on the ramp like he'd linger before he walked over to our house, I knew my missiles would strike him in the chest, pierce his dark and burnt flesh.

I needed him to hurt, so I kneeled behind my grandmother's van and jammed as many branches into the muffler as I could. I was in a groove, pushing my bundle deeper in, watching my hands become black, until I heard the question, "¿Qué haces ahí?" I looked around and there was my grandmother at the doorway, her arms akimbo, her head tilted at a sharp, what-the-hell-is-happening angle. I dropped the sticks and ran to the middle of the yard, wiping my hands on my shorts.

"Why are you doing that?' she asked, her English choppy, harsh. "Why?" she repeated, but I didn't answer. I didn't know how to. "No se por que haces cosa así. I'm going to tell your mom. Take them out," she demanded, pointing at the van. "Sácalos ahorra."

I ran back and began pulling them out, regretting my eagerness to fill the muffler.. I shouldn't have stuffed so many. I wanted to turn around and look at Santos' house, but I heard my grandmother approaching, her huaraches scraping the patches of parched Bermuda grass constellated on the border of her lawn. I stuck my tiny hands deeper into the muffler, pulling hard on the branches I thought would hit the hardest when they shot out. My grandmother came behind me and I stood up. "It's not right you do that," she said, crouching to inspect the muffler. "Lo puedes quebrar." There'd be other moments when my actions wouldn't be right either, when I'd break the springs on the screen door, be careless with her angel figurines, or the one time when I placed both of my hands on the bathroom sink and pushed my body up so I could get a better look at myself in the mirror, only to hear a sudden snap of enameled cast-iron collapsing beneath my weight. My list would grow, but never would anything feel this deserving of punishment, of my grandmother's anger.

Back in the yard, my grandmother continued shouting. I watched on, wondering if the fight would ever end. My uncles lifted Santos and began shoving him back and forth. He was spent. Blood blotted his white shirt. Blades of grass speckled his face. His hair was ruffled, exposing part of his burnt neck, and he looked even drunker than he had earlier.

"Leave!" shouted Jaime, tossing him down and kicking the back of his thigh as he tried to crawl away. Santos stood up, stumbled a bit, placed his right arm on my grandmother's van, seeking a semblance of breath.

"Fuck you," was all he could manage. My uncles moved closer. He coughed, wiped the snot that hung from his nose, licked his lips, and then turned around, backpedaling out of the driveway.

"Don't come around again," said Javi. Santos waved his hand incoherently in front of his chest and walked back to his mother's house, looking at the asphalt the whole way.

My uncles stared him down. We all did. I don't remember the discussion afterwards, or if there was one. What I do remember is the funeral home, years later, greeting people I didn't know, entering through a heavy set of doors. The people in the pews turning around to stare. My mother was behind me, pushing me along, and at the far end, I saw my aunt Rosa and my cousins Ricky and Eloy. They were smiling, happy to see me. We sat down with them, but before I knew it I was standing in front of Santos. He appeared safe, respectable, decent in a white button-down. Though he was dark-skinned, he looked pasty, like burnt candle wax, and I caught a glimpse of exactly what Eloy had whispered to me: half of his head is shaved. I bowed my head, mouthed an Our Father and looked up, tiptoeing for a better angle. I was alone. My mother, my aunts, and the other side of my family were all by the door, talking, hugging, giving each other condolences. I placed my hands in front of me. I looked back, but they didn't. I circled around the casket until I saw the line where his hair once was. I thought of Two-Face from Batman. I thought something seemed off. And as

I took a few more steps, bit the inside of my lower lip, I saw the gash, the scar, the slither of stitched flesh measuring just as long as my hand. I studied it, noted how fresh it still appeared, how forceful the impact was, feeling as though I was the one who caused this. My mother later told me that he was involved in a drug deal gone wrong, that he didn't pay up, or tried to sell a product that didn't weigh the right amount. Whatever it was, the investigation concluded he was forced to kneel, to face his executioner and the ax that struck the side of his head, made him bleed out. I backed away and walked down the aisle.

In the reception room, small groups of adults were talking to one another, shifting their bodies, elaborating with hand gestures. Ricky and Eloy were laughing, running around a sofa just off to the side, playing tag or whatever game that seemed acceptable for their age. People took turns carrying my sister, bringing her head to their shoulders, kissing her cheeks.

The day Santos was buried, we went home and packed a Styrofoam cooler with sodas, bologna, cheese, and bread into our van. I sat in the backseat, while Iris rested in the car seat next to me. With the windows halfway down, my mother seemed somber. But there were no tears to compliment the mood I thought she was feeling. Half an hour on the road and she told us we were going to Six Flags.

"What? In San Antonio?" I asked.

"Yes. Six Flags," she said. "In San Antonio. You excited?"

Our eyes met in the rearview mirror and I nodded.

My sister turned to me and smiled.

BUSTER

They were always up early. Always roaming the streets in that slow, incoherent pace displayed by vagabonds who wander from alley to alley rifling through trash bins, burying their hands deeper through labyrinths of folded cardboard, soda cans, coffee cups, black and white bags overflowing with scraps of uneaten or expired food already claimed by maggots, rats, by halo upon halo of flies. They thrived on little to no sleep, like my grandmother, who every morning lumbered to the backyard to feed them. On nights when I'd sleep over, I'd sometimes hear her struggling to open her bedroom door, coughing and bumping into chairs and opening drawers throughout the kitchen, where a pot of coffee was set and the stove turned on to warm the house. She'd move a few items around the table, straighten the plastic tablecloth, the stained, embroidered placemats, the empty vase that would occasionally host a small bouquet of seasonal flowers she'd pluck from her garden, giving the viewer the impression that her kitchen matched those simple yet glossy kitchens one could find in the pages of waiting room magazines.

From the Pine-Sol scented hallway, I'd see her silhouette drag the large bag of Kibbles 'n Bits resting by the refrigerator and head out the door. I'd slip into the kitchen, move from shadow to shadow until I'd arrive at the half-opened window, prop my chin on the windowsill, and gaze at the dogs running toward her diabetic legs—each hungry, eager, panting as they'd huddle into a swarm. There must have been about twelve or fifteen. I never counted. Some were large, the size of Great Danes, while others had bodies that fell between the builds of Dachshunds, Border Collies, and Boxers. Only two, a Rottweiler named Max and a Labrador-looking mix named Dalia, were hers, or more specifically, my twin teenage uncles', who merely interacted with them whenever they'd show them off to friends. They'd grip either Max or Dalia by the chain collar and tell them to sic whoever was standing closest, releasing the chain little by little the higher they jumped. It somehow seemed funny then, to watch how quickly their friends jolted back, to notice how they'd laugh, attempting to hide the nervousness that suddenly overtook their bodies, made them reluctant to come near my uncles even after they tied their beasts up.

After stepping out of the kitchen, my grandmother led the group of dogs with her slow walk to the center of the yard, where a cluster of plastic and metal bowls rested, some which I remember eating from. "Siéntate. Sit," she'd say, patting the air with her left hand, while her right gripped the top of the bag. A few would begin barking, nudging it with their noses, pawing at the pictured dogs eating their well-proportioned share in a manner that appeared overtly suburban. My grandmother would squat lower, open the bag, then, lifting as high as she could, pour it poorly into the bowls. She'd thoroughly shake the end of the bag, wiggle her body, and although it didn't seem like she could miss, most would spill onto the grass, forming mounds that resembled anthills just after a storm.

Then began the feast. They'd bow their heads to the altar of cheap dog food, a combination of large pieces mixed with hard ones they'd struggle to chew, swallow, to comfortably eat. Sometimes, some of them—new dogs or dogs that hadn't been by for a while—would devour their portions too quickly, gag, and vomit everything out. They'd stare at it, lick the gooey edges, and after a few sniffs of that yellow, green, and red gunk that looked like dyed diarrhea, they'd go back to eating it, unconcerned with its taste or consistency.

My grandmother would close the bag, drag it back to the doorsteps, then turn around and watch them, her arms crossed in front of her chest. It was around this point that dawn would erase her silhouette, revealing her short stature, frizzy hair, her old and partly vitiligo flesh. I was halfway out of the kitchen, not wanting to be caught, but I too would stop and imagine that she was smiling at what she'd never claim was the good deed she had just done.

In the afternoon, however, her sympathy was nowhere to be found. They had a habit of pulling down the clothes from the clothesline, snatching pairs of socks, button-downs, corduroys, khakis, jeans, blouses, bras, wife-beaters and boxer briefs they'd reach if they jumped high enough, or if the wind, like an accomplice, would push them just over the line, make each article of clothing dangle at an angle perfect for their jowls.

Out in the center of the yard again, my grandmother would try to shoo them away, swiping her kitchen towel at their snouts, swinging her broom at their legs, cursing them in English and Spanish, as though her mixed dialect had the power to make them scatter, hide behind the shed, send them running to the chain-link fence, where they'd bend their visibly crooked spines, stretch their bodies out like Chinese finger traps, and dart down the same alleyway most of them spent their nights, aware now that the breakfast provided wasn't a guarantee that they'd always be allowed to stay.

Regardless if they were new or not, if they had collars or were ownerless when they showed up, they were her dogs, her mange-infested nomads, her matted strays, her four-legged mutts she no longer wanted to support, fatigued with performing the sweetheart in the morning, witch in the afternoon routine every day.

Though it seemed like she could keep up the pace, her grandmother instinct would eventually kick in, and after a few minutes of swiping with no particular dog in mind, of shouting vulgarities that sounded like loud prayers, she'd lose the vigor to smack them as hard as I knew she could. Her relaxed attitude was, I thought, a reflection, of the way she felt about my uncles, who, though still a year away from graduating high school, didn't have any short- or long-term plans to leave home. College wasn't a discussion in their household, neither was the serious possibility that they would move out, get a place of their own. No, they were toward the bottom on a list of nine children—my aunt Irene being the youngest—and the only thing expected of them was to get a job once they graduated, which, if I remember correctly, they did—Jaime as a secretary at a supposed insurance agency, Javi at the city's water plant, which was conveniently located only a few blocks from our neighborhood.

For the dogs, my grandmother was queen. Not even I, whose hands and shoes they'd sometimes lick, pausing to see if I'd toss them anything that resembled food, was interesting enough for them. The feeling was mutual. I could bear their proximity, in how heavily they'd pant, in how ugly they looked, mucus hanging from the corner of their eyelids, hand-sized patches of hair missing, matted, covering their gnat-swollen faces in such a way that they'd have to crane their necks upwards to get a better look at their surroundings. I could see their ribs, their shoulder blades, their crooked spines, their emaciated bodies whose only source of sustenance was that one haphazardly poured meal a day. I was careful around them and they could sense it, and although I wanted to feel guilty, give them our leftovers of spaghetti, ready-made chicken, beans and weenies, or Hamburger Helper that would sit for weeks, even months, in our fridge, I never regretted how relieved I'd feel when I'd decide not to act. I was merely a spectator, and if I was in the yard, I kept my distance, reminding myself, as my mother would often warn, that at any time they could snap, find issue with the way I moved or how long I stared, increasing the chances of them attacking, of getting rabies or some rabid-like disease that would require a visit to the emergency room and twelve large shots to the middle of the stomach, treatment we probably couldn't afford. I thought maybe my grandmother was immune and didn't mind kicking them when necessary, pinching the back of their necks, or if they were small enough, tossing them to some other part of the yard. There'd be times when it was a puppy, a mixed-breed that was most likely born in the alley, already accustomed to digging through Hefty bags around trash bins for scraps, learning that whenever it would whine and scratch the backdoor, my grandmother was merely going to grab it and place it back over the fence, hoping it wouldn't find its way back.

Despite my grandmother's persistence, the new arrivals to the yard had it the easiest. They could leave at their own will, could eat a few free meals and travel to the next house, attempt to elicit sympathy from those more willing to entertain their cries. Dalia and Max couldn't. They remained tied to the splintered pole of what appeared to be that half-shed, half-garage where my uncles housed those used Impalas they'd remodel into low-riders, adding any type of modification that increased their street cred.

There was also a large barbecue pit inside, and I remember Max and Dalia resting by it whenever either one of my uncles was cooking for family gatherings, waiting to be thrown chicken or pork chop bones, or any undesirable piece of meat that smelled more enticing than even the freshest bag of Kibbles 'n Bits. Though the chains and ropes became longer over the years, and they were able to play with the other dogs, chase them around, and roam the periphery of our yard—since there was no fence that divided my grandparents' house with ours—they'd live their short lives and die near the shed.

My own dog Buster would share the same fate, if fate—whether I believed in the concept or not—could be extended to dogs. Buster wasn't a male like the name would suggest, but a female my aunt and uncle had originally named Bertha, a name that at least in my mind at the time was appropriate for her short, stocky legs, her wide body, her robust snout that resembled the snout of a Bull Terrier. She was black with tobacco-brown around her jaw, stomach, ears, legs, and paws. I received her for my birthday, my seventh if I'm not mistaken, and because I had been wanting a dog for some time—a dog unlike the ones huddled around my grandmother's legs every morning—my aunt and uncle saw no problem in giving her to me, feeling not only that I was old enough to take care of a dog, but also, as I'd one day learn, that this was the easiest way to get rid of her without taking her to the pound, or dropping her off on the outskirts of town like some of my other aunts had done to dogs they could no longer provide for, love. Bertha was old and hadn't meshed well with my aunt's other two dogs—a black Lab named Shadow and a brown one, Fudge—both of whom were hunting dogs I only ever got to know on trips with my uncles and cousins, dogs around whom I was never truly comfortable.

Shadow was the bigger of the two, always hyper, always ready to retrieve whatever object my cousins, Roy and Chris, threw in his direction. Fudge was by far calmer, younger, a follower by every dog standard, and a bit lazier when it came to fetching dead birds from the bushes. Because I felt my mother felt that I felt what I can only describe as a sense of paternal incompleteness, since there was no father in my life with which I could do these kinds of things, she insisted that I partake in more manly activities, that I learn what it felt like to handle a shotgun, shit in the woods, kill a bird and pluck it of its feathers so I could experience what she saw as the necessary steps to manhood, as though one of the ways to fulfill this role was through the death of small animals. I never understood the joy of it, though, the hours we spent sitting, craning our necks at the rows of trees extending for miles across another expanse of unnamed backcountry, watching as we all turned into silhouettes when dusk washed over us with whatever symbolism we ascribed to it, and jumping up to shoot at a flock of white-wings that, if close enough, fell as we expected.

Shadow and Fudge would retrieve them, and we'd arrive home well into the night with the quotas my uncle and cousins had set for themselves before we left. I always fell short, having first started off with a BB gun, and moved up only after a year to single-shot 20 gauge I was never able to reload as quickly as my cousins. Nevertheless, I racked up my share, and I stood with them plucking the feathers, breaking off the wings, decapitating the heads, and occasionally tossing their remains like a baseball with Roy and Chris. Once, while I was digging through the ice chest full of dead white-wings, searching for one that wasn't too bloody or battered with BBs, Chris snuck up behind me and placed the handful of discarded wings, heads, and tails inside my shirt collar. I felt something cold, and thinking it was ice, I grabbed and pulled on my shirttail, knowing that since I was the youngest of the three, I was the easiest target for their jokes, for their comments that I preferred guys to girls, for their double teaming efforts when we played *007* on Nintendo 64, or for my gullibility each time they propped an old painting of a clown on a chair next to the bed whenever I'd sleep over, so that when they blew in my ears, I'd wake up and stare at a white-painted face with orange hair patched on the sides of his head, ruffs collared extravagantly on his neck, and lipstick that extended deep into his cheeks. As my eyes would shudder into focus, my imagination would take over, and I'd see the clown's mouth opening, his jaw dislocating, his canines and incisors growing longer, as if filed, and his head turning, tilting, pushing past the wooden frame and canvas in some *It*-type of fashion that never failed to get me to jolt out of bed, screaming that I had enough of their shit, that this wasn't funny anymore.

I reached my hand beneath the back of my shirt and pulled out a lump of blood, feathers, severed wings, and a small head with a crushed beak. I thought there was a large gash on my back that I hadn't felt, and this black bile and bones were spilling from it. I tossed the lump on their backyard porch and Shadow came running over to lick it, see if it was something he could eat. When he looked up at me, as though I should have dropped something with more flavor, I remembered our first encounter. It was a year before I got Buster. Like a game show host revealing the grand prize, my aunt opened the back door of her house, said all I had to do was step outside, be myself, pretend my presence was something natural. Shadow and Fudge needed to familiarize their noses with my scent, understand that I would be accompanying them on their hunting trips, and would be expecting them to retrieve the birds I killed. My mother walked me to the back door. I could hear Roy and Chris laughing outside.

"It's so he feels comfortable," said my uncle. "And plus, they've gotta learn to trust him when he's out there." My uncle was short, stocky, had a lazy left eye, and was balding. He smelled like Bud Light, and always carried a cold can in a koozie while barbecuing, watching the Cowboys or the Astros, or in between every arbitrary break when we were out in the backcountry, rewarding himself with another for another two or three white-wings he had just shot down.

"They won't do nothing," said my aunt. "Sólo brincan. Es todo que hacen. They just jump, that's all. They don't bite." Although her English and Spanish were somewhat reassuring, I couldn't picture myself being natural around them, pulling their tails or poking their ribs like my cousins so often would when they were trying to get them to bark, or even jacking them off in a game of truth and dare, which they were always so eager to play, pretending they had no other choice but to pick dare every time.

That wasn't me, and there was no way to change who I thought I was when my uncle opened the door. I walked toward it, measuring my breaths, gripping my hand in front of me, and trying to find an object to focus on: the water hose, the upturned Frisbees, the plants, the trees. Before I got to the porch, however, Shadow rushed to the door and jumped on me. I put my hands in front of my face and turned away, but he had already dug his nails into my shirt and was scratching at my chest, my shoulders, my neck. He opened his mouth, flashed his canines. I backpedaled and stumbled on the tile floor, breaking my fall with my elbows.

"Shadow! Shadow!" my uncle yelled. "Get off, boy!" His voice was loud but there was no urgency to it. He didn't feel the same stress one should feel when they are watching a person getting mauled, or at least a person whose body gave every indication that he thought he was getting mauled. I waved my hands at his face, attempting to push off. "Stop! Stop!" I yelled, but Shadow mistook my crying for enthusiasm, and the licks and drool dripping onto my cheeks continued. I began kicking, squirming beneath his legs, shouting I wasn't sure what. I thought my uncle, aunt, and cousins were laughing, pointing, tossing their heads back, disappointed that I couldn't handle a dog. And although they would, indeed, tease me later that afternoon when we were seated at the table and my trembling settled with a spoonful of salt my aunt insisted would get me under control, they all, with the exception of my mother, helped pull Shadow off.

I laid there, sprawled in what my aunt would later claim was an exaggeration, angled in the notion that I wasn't really scared at all, since she too had seen the dogs at my grandparents' house and had noticed me lingering out there on more than a few occasions, but merely faking it because I wanted to be perceived as a boy who was fearful of dogs, who didn't know how to express his reluctance to go on hunting trips, who didn't feel any desire to shoot a gun, and this was the easiest way to convince my mother that an activity involving a dog like Shadow wasn't the activity for me.

"He didn't do nothing to you. All he wanted to do was play," she said, reaching over to touch my forearm, letting me know that everything was okay. My mother stepped into the bathroom, while my uncle went out back to speak to Roy and Chris.

"Why were you scared?" she asked.

"He – he – I thought he was – was going to bite me," I stuttered, still shaking, wiping the tears that had collected around my jaw.

"But he wasn't, Stevie. He wasn't."

"I thought he was," I said, managing not to bawl again as I could still feel Shadow's large body pressed against me, swiping at my face.

"He wasn't, Esteban. You understand?" she said, saying my real name in that accented way my mother would say it when her tone became more serious.

"You don't need to be scared. You want to go hunting with them and you're scared. Come on now. Ya. You're what, ten years old?"

"Ni – nine years," I said.

"You're nine years old and you're still scared of dogs." She chuckled and leaned back on the chair. There were paper plates of barbecue resting between us, and paper cups half filled with soda, Gatorade, and water that I wanted to pick up and throw at her, say that she wasn't the one beneath Shadow, he wasn't jumping on her, scratching her shirt, throwing his weight against her ribs, baring his teeth so close to her face that there was no way not to think he was going to tear right through it, redefine and rearrange the features that defined who she thought she was.

She smiled and shook her head. "Esteban, Esteban, Esteban," she said. "If you don't want to go hunting, you don't have to."

"I do, I – I do," I insisted. For a moment, neither of us spoke, my sniffles interrupting what would have otherwise been a needed silence.

"Okay," she said, nodding her head. She stared at the floor, examined my imitation Nikes, and then moved onto my blue jean shorts and striped blue and yellow polo, perhaps mentally comparing my clothes with what her sons were now into, the Doc Martins, American Eagle, white seashell necklaces, hair gel with minimal flaking, and cologne that didn't wear off easily. I barely even wore deodorant.

Perhaps she felt pity when she agreed to give me Bertha, had sensed that I was always wary around Shadow and Fudge, and that an older dog, one whose excitement only came in spurts, would fit me best. Whatever her reasons, she seemed enthusiastic when I took Bertha home. I was too, but I found myself worried about her name, how I would tell others at school that I had a dog named Bertha. Bertha brought to mind a large, unmarried, short-haired German woman who spent her afternoons on the porch smoking pack after pack of cigarettes. Bertha reminded me of a train. A machine. A massive object whose only purpose was to take up space. It reminded me of Principal Trunchball from the movie *Matilda*, and even though I thought there was a slight resemblance—same rigidness, same frame—I couldn't bring myself to pronounce that name.

"Can I change it?" I asked my mother on our way back from my aunt's house. Bertha was in the backseat with me, tongue out, panting, looking out the van window. "I want to change her name to Buster."

"Buster's a boy's name," said my mother. "You can't change a boy's name to a girl's."

"What about the name Pat?" I asked.

"What about it?"

"That's a boy's and a girl's name."

"It's a girl's name."

"Pat can stand for Patrick, too."

"No. Patrick stands for Patrick."

"Nuh uh."

"Yes. It sounds ugly to call a boy Pat."

I watched Bertha rest her head on the seat. She looked at me, timid with the sharp turns and increasing speed. I wanted to pet her, but I was timid, too, unsure how she would react. I had petted her before, given her leftover pieces of bread, or ready-made chicken that smelled like it had been sitting for weeks in the fridge, but I was still a stranger then, a figure that came and went, devoid of significance. I stared hard at Bertha, wondering if she sensed what my mother and I were discussing.

"How about when we get you a boy dog?" my mother said.

"What do you mean?"

"I mean after Bertha, we can get a boy dog and name him Buster."

"After? What do you mean after?" I was acting as though I

didn't know what *after* meant, aware there was no doggie heaven or special doggie hospital as mothers were apt to explain to their children when they began asking where their Baileys, Dukes, Buddys, Luckys, Lucys, Lolas were, if not in their backyard. I knew that dogs died, people died, plants died, objects died when there was no longer any use for them, and I too would die when I got to be as old as my grandfather, though I imagined I'd be as blind, would be able to move around by myself, and would know who every member of family was without having to ask. Bertha would die and because she would die, I needed to name her Buster.

My mother hesitated, pretending to concentrate on the road. "Why Buster? I've always liked Nelson for a boy. I was almost gonna name you Nelson but your grandpa had a best friend named Esteban who had just passed away and he was depressed about it for a long time. I could tell he wanted me to name you after him. He was dropping hints, mentioning his friend more and more the closer I was to having you. I'm glad I did. Esteban fits you good." I didn't respond, already familiar with this story. "Fine. You can name her Buster," she said, partially turning around. I tried not to smile, mumbling a half-hearted "Thank you." I reached over to touch the top of Buster's head, but she pulled away and repositioned the upper half of her body closer to her hind legs. I settled for her neck.

And her neck was what I'd be settling for when we arrived home. My grandmother's de facto dogs were roaming the stretch of yard between our house and hers. Some were resting beneath the long shadow casted by my grandparents' roof. Others were by the clothesline, pawing and gnawing on each other's necks. I opened the van's side door, and before I could clip the leash to Buster's collar, she jumped out and trotted to the middle of the yard, where two dogs met her and began their thorough process of sniffing as much of her body as they could, moving from the side of her face to her legs to her ass, one directly behind her, one squatting beneath her stomach. Buster looked around, patient, acquainted with the ritual, having done her fair share. A few other dogs—a white one that resembled a dirty mattress, a light brown one with patches of hair missing and old scabs that seemed to have never healed around his eyes, and another whose paws were clearly aching, black with what I could only guess was dried blood—came up to her and took their turns.

For the first time, I noticed her teats, how swollen and leather-black they were, how they resembled the other female dogs that had given birth. I imagined, considering their closeness to the ground, the way they swung back and forth as she trotted the yard, that she had perhaps fed her pups longer than her body should have allowed.

"Buster," I called. "Bertha, come, come." I stood there waiting, while my mother walked over and began shooing them away, shouting "Move, move!" They moved back, responding the same way they did to my grandmother. My mother leaned over, grabbed Buster by the collar, and pulled her back to the driveway, her nails scraping the concrete.

"I don't want her inside the house."

"Why not?" I asked, taking a hold of Buster.

"Because she smells and she might start tearing up the couches. Tie her in the back."

"But can she come inside sometimes?"

"Maybe, we'll discuss it. You already named her Buster." She smiled and went inside. I clipped the leash and led her around the other side of the house, hoping the dogs wouldn't follow us.

When we got to the shed, they stood, in groups of two or three, about twenty feet away, watching as I flattened the weeds and grass with my foot, looped the leash around the corner cinder block, and tied it tightly. The leash was short and gave her hardly any room to move. I placed my hands on the splintered door with the streaked remnants of yellow paint that once glazed the shed, thinking I could find a rope inside to substitute for the leash. My grandfather built our house, and it was his and my grandmother's before he built their new house right beside it. When I'd return home from college a decade later, I'd sometimes drive through our old neighborhood, slow down and stare at our house, trying to remember how the parched Bermuda grass felt on my face, forearms, and hands every time I fell playing tag with my cousins in the front yard, how the air-conditioning unit leaked on the porch, forming a blackened pool of water that turned into mold, how the linoleum inside creaked and cracked like arthritic bone with each step we took, how we'd have to lift the lid of the toilet and jerk the lever so it would flush, how our shower was a mass of dark concrete my grandfather never got around to smoothing out, or how only a blanket nailed to the wall separated my room from my mother's and stepfather's, doing little to suppress the moans and snores that so often kept me awake.

The shed was just as dilapidated, a relic without the viewers and consensus to give its rotten, crosshatched frame both value and meaning. The door opened with the same suspense doors open in movies, preempting the villain's appearance a scene or two later. Of course there were oddly-angled cobwebs along the edges, each speckled with a history of insects my gooseflesh skin couldn't help but feel were still alive. Two slits of light from the corners cuts across the floor, forming a kind of X that partly illuminated the contents inside: the blue, mold-blotched tarps folded haphazardly and piled against the wall, a lawn mower turned on its side to reveal a broken blade that appeared as though it had hit and failed to pierce objects unwilling to budge from their form, a ladder with a few steps missing, the rails from an old bed frame, tattered lawn chairs, scattered and poorly sawed 2x4s, open boxes of nails rusted from years of rain, metal and plastic pipes that could have served a number of purposes, but that now rested untouched like the group of lidless stock pots stacked toward the back, where just above, hung a line of bike chains, orange extension cords, and tattered rope I walked closer toward, knowing that even if I tied the flared ends together, they'd still be too short for Buster.

I walked back out and tried to loosen the leash. The dogs had inched closer, their quick sniffs perhaps enough to initiate Buster into the group. They were waiting for her to join, to roam the yard, the neighborhood, the alleyway, to swarm my grandmother every morning. I petted the side of her head, and then tried, like my mother, to shoo the other dogs away, weakly shouting, "Move. Leave her alone." They didn't seem to hear, or didn't want to, and even as I moved closer, they stood still, focused on Buster. I saw no point in continuing, so I moved back, farther, father. Weeks passed, and I found myself still backpedaling down the yard, watching her interact with the dogs, often escaping from the leash, so that every time my mother and I came home from work and school, we'd each attempt to catch her, my mother taking one side, me the other, our sloppy movements rendering us into a kind of circus act. Recalling it now, I can almost hear the banjo music playing in the background.

Sometimes my sister would try to help us, zigzagging through the yard with her short stride, four-years old and unafraid of how close the dogs would crowd her legs, how they'd chase playfully after her, bite and pull her unstrapped Velcro shoe straps, at times causing her to fall, laugh, to get back up, and run after the dog she assumed was Buster. Though we were able to retrieve Buster, tie her back to the shed, we both gave up, and I'd only walk over to feed her, stay till she finished at least half of her bowl.

As an anthropology major in college, I learned that the one thing humans and canines excel at equally is fucking. Not long after I renamed her, Buster's stomach started swelling, her behavior became sluggish, her demeanor reserved. She plopped on the ground any chance she could. My mother explained how the birds and the bees worked, sitting me at the table and drawing diagrams and two-dimensional figures on notebook paper, explaining that most animals, regardless of how large, small, or strangely shaped their anatomies were, had the same basic reproductive parts. But the concept still seemed foreign, still seemed like something left to anatomy textbooks, a practice people did in the darkness because the darkness was the only thing that could bear witness to their contortions, moans, secrets. And when I had seen the dogs do it, it was on nightly street corners where they'd hump beneath the lamppost's orange glow, get their asses locked together by the curb, squirm and shake their bodies and pull away from each other like a Chinese finger trap. Buster became somewhat friendlier—rubbing against my legs, as though she were apologizing for her cold introduction, searching for sympathy—and then isolated herself from the other dogs, one of which had gotten her pregnant.

My grandmother told my mother it'd be best if we got rid of her, that they were a burden, would only breed and fuck and give you another litter of burdens neither my mother nor I were in the positions to handle. I can only imagine how the conversation played out, each standing by my window in my grandmother's kitchen, gossiping about the latest problems my aunts were facing with their children, as I'd usually overhear them discussing, and somehow finding a way to compare them with the dogs, saying that because my younger cousins weren't being looked after—at least in the way she would have expected and done—they looked homeless, their hair disheveled, their teeth yellowed, unbrushed, their faces dirtied from tossing themselves around in the yard all day. I imagine this going on for some time before my grandmother realized her tangent and maneuvered the conversation back into talk about the dogs, advising my mother that I was just a child and children couldn't take care of children—her daughters couldn't even take care of theirs—and if she got rid of Buster quickly I wouldn't remember her later on, since the memory of her would be too short to piece back together in any meaningful way.

"I don't want her if she's pregnant," said my mother as we pulled into the driveway one day.

"I think she's just eating too much. I'll feed her less."

"You know she's pregnant, Esteban." She shut the engine off, dislodged the keys from the ignition. "Mijo, you don't have time, especially with baseball every day. We get home late. We can barely take care of her now. Now imagine when she has puppies. It's too much."

"We'll just give them away," I said, bending my glove inward, outward, knowing I'd have to microwave it a few more times before it molded fluently to my hand.

"It's not that easy," she said. "It's . . . it's different with dogs." I stared hard at my glove, feeling as though my mother were looking at me, trying to get a reaction. "Well," she sighed, "let's just hope she's not pregnant." As her stomach enlarged, and her teats starting sagging, swaying swine-like near the ground, we didn't discuss it further, each of us aware that she was sleeping for weeks on the side of the shed before she moved permanently beneath it, remaining there throughout the days leading up to the birth of her litter.

I remember hearing the whimpers, how close and yet how far they sounded, how sharp and sudden they echoed throughout our yard. Dusk, like a wound reopened so much it had lost its ability to heal, was blotting through the crosshatched columns of clouds that appeared to have been borrowed directly from a motivational poster. A few dogs were barking, snapping at the wind, while others were lying on the ground with their heads tilted, their ears raised every time another wail seeped form beneath the shed. There were clothes on my grandparents' clothesline, swaying with a symbolism I couldn't quite figure out. I could feel my legs taking over, could feel my body walking closer, squatting with each step, placing my hands and knees on the sandpaper-sharp grass, attempting to mute my breathing, to stifle the curiosity that made me lower my head, as I rested my chin and cheek by the cinder block and ground, and thrust my face into that fetal darkness. I waited for my eyes to come into focus. I blinked rapidly, squinted harder, harder, until I was able to see two flickering bulbs of light swinging side to side. I thought I said *Buster*, but my breath only grew heavier as the wails grew louder. Buster started growling, and I could see her canines flashing through the fleshy folds of her jowls. A whimper stabbed the darkness that was still masking the more definitive features of Buster's face, and she leaned over and licked the pup beneath her, stretching her tongue across its head, across that afterbirth of slime and goo that enveloped her tiny body. Three or four pups squirmed besides the other. Buster licked them too but stopped when I pushed myself farther in, my head and shoulders well beneath the shed. She growled again, and just as I thought she was going to lunge at me, bark and bite my hands, she raised the upper half of her body, as much as the space allowed her to rise, and repositioned her head so it faced the other way. I tried to call out her name again, but my voice was muffled by the mist of dirt pulsing to the rhythm of my breath, and by the pups wailing for their mother's attention. She didn't give in, however, perhaps too fatigued with pushing them out of her body. A part of me wanted to reach out and grab them, cradle them in my arms, feed them bottles of milk, wrap them in towels as they slept and cried and thought that my chest was the warmth of their mother's stomach. But that was something I knew I wasn't ready for, that I feared more than desired.

The wailing persisted. Buster stayed silent. I backed out slowly, and as I hit my head on the shed, I thought I saw the pups squirming toward me, moving through the dirt like maggots who had finished with one body and were blindly looking for the next. I hit my head again and slithered out of the shed, standing up and stumbling as I tried to backpedal from the scene. I turned around and ran to the undefined edge of the yard, then looked back, feeling as though the whimpers were not real but merely a recording, like cries from a baby monitor. The clouds thinned out, scalping what remained of the sun. My grandmother's dogs had moved back, and I fell somewhere in between, unsure if the wailing would ever stop.

PALLBEARERS

I thought the wailing would never stop. The wails of my mother, grandmother, my uncles and aunts. The wails of unknown relatives whose names I forgot the moment they leaned over, rubbed my cheeks or shoulder, and introduced themselves when they first arrived at the funeral home as So-and-So, telling my mother how much I looked like my grandfather, how they were surprised that I shared the same features that defined him: a light-complexion, an oval-shaped head, an overall demeanor that brought to mind the most casual of interactions, and that prompted what I can now see as a sigh of relief spreading across their faces, expressing how comforted they were that at least someone in the family embodied the memory of his physical characteristics, since the image we all attached to the man, the descriptions that came to mind when his name was mentioned, was just as important as every intangible impression he left behind. Before my relatives, however, pulled away, each becoming another indistinguishable figure among the crowd, taking their sympathy with them, I stared curiously at the dark and hieroglyphic folds and wrinkles webbed from their foreheads to their cheeks, jaws, chins, and down into the sharp cliffs of their necks, where the skin sagged just enough for my ten-year-old mind to think that in a few weeks' time, that hanging flap of flesh would turn into a full-fledged wattle. They all appeared to already be gobbling, mumbling sentences that in between the sniffs, the sighs, the tears that were unable to find a meaningful path, made no sense. I couldn't understand the subtleties of their body language. I couldn't infer an explanation when they said *Complicado, tan complicado*, and although I knew the English equivalent, it was still difficult to tease out what they meant when their lips—dry, thin, foaming at the corners with saliva—sounded like a broken windup box that dwindled but never ended. *Complicado, tan complicado.*

In the reception room, the mood was mournful, but the kind of mournful that goes out to eat after the burial, sits at a table and orders a bacon cheeseburger, extra fries, a large soda, and a brownie à la mode that on any other day would have been skipped for the check. I had not yet learned to compartmentalize my feelings in that manner, had not yet found solace in silence, or in short, cliché quotes echoing that *life goes on* sentiment that seemed to have put everyone at ease in the room, where I stood watching more family members file in, noting the formulaic manner in which their limbs moved when they embraced each other, nodded their heads, forced a smile that was adequate for the somber disposition created by the dim lamps and lights, the gray carpet that looked like elephant hide, and the brown, sunken sofas positioned at each corner.

The sofas were like the ones at my stepfather's funeral, and just as I had studied them back then, I studied these particular leather cushions now, certain they carried the scent of lint-speckled pants, jeans, shirttails, jackets, peacoats, black pantyhose, different sized hands resting and pushing off of them, a whole history of temporary sitters that took a break from the ritual before getting back up and fulfilling the role they were expected to fulfill. Everything in that room, from the desk to the water fountains that spurted back on themselves regardless of how hard someone pushed, had a history to share, and it demanded that we share ours too, that we let this room hold the nuances of our actions long after we had left. Though I tried not to personify it, to see the room merely as a space that wouldn't capture what occurred that day, I knew it would bear the conversations, the head tilts, the head shakes, the embraces, the shifting and restless postures, the muffled laughs, the shoes scraping across the carpet, the thud of the doors opening, closing, opening, and the uncanny sense, spilling from the main room, that we had all been here before in some shape or form.

It felt like déjà vu, and that sensation carried over to the church, the same church where throughout middle school, I attended CCD every Wednesday, sat with Bobby and Luis making dick jokes about the saints and random authority figures painted across the ceiling, suggesting that the small bumps on their robes looked larger than the bumps on our crotches. We'd bow our heads, feign another prayer, kneel in the pew, look up as though we were receiving divine intervention, and criticize Jesus' loincloth, saying that it wasn't wrinkled and rugged enough for someone who appeared to have been whipped, sentenced, ridiculed, and forced to drag a cross for miles upon miles across Roman land. It looked too perfect, ordered, all the paintings did, and there was no lesson these poorly rendered, half-clothed men immortalized in brushstrokes could instill in us when all we wanted to do was talk, make each other laugh, speak about the latest girl we liked, and pretend to feel as though we were sinners only when the sermon was about to end.

The funeral priest looked hazy, disfigured, like a cubist painting, or an out-of-focus Polaroid found behind the plastic sheets of photo albums taken out only when distant relatives visited. Mere flashes of his face remain, the bushy eyebrows, the cracked and clay-colored skin that resembled roadside pottery no one ever bought, the angle at which his neck twisted inside that clerical collar as he looked side to side, addressed the seated congregation for no more than fifteen minutes, slowly building up my grandfather's life, describing his character as though he knew him personally, saying, *Santiago was aware of his sins, knew the faults he had as a father, as a man, and yet his outlook on the world remained devoutly Catholic.* My grandfather never attended church, at least that I knew of, but the priest's words were enough to move my family, to get them to start crying, coughing, contorting their seated bodies in the same nervous manner reserved for children. And as I sat there imaging what it must feel like to talk about someone whose organs had been removed, whose embalmed flesh would rot in a casket, and who lived his last few years nearly blind, limited to the light that filtered through the yellowish film of discharge that lined his eyes, the priest again commented on what a *great man*, what a *fair father*, what a *loving husband* he was, inciting wails from my mother, my grandmother, my uncles and aunts, and from my unknown relatives whose tears at the funeral home now appeared beyond their control.

I remember speeding down the aisle with my sister Iris, who— four years younger than me and dressed in the same black puffy dress she'd use for more than one Wal-Mart family photo— seemed just as unsure as I was if that was all there was to this fast-food version of a service. I was expecting the priest to conduct the ceremony at the gravesite, for the scene at the gravesite to play out the way it does in films, focusing first on the priest or priest-like figure who, in a stoic and baritone voice, methodically recites scripture, becomes deep, speaks over the claps of thunder, and crosses both himself and the deceased beneath a black umbrella, as the camera moves at different angles throughout the crowd, zooming in on the slashes of rain that offer the perfect segue for the scene to slowly fade out. For a moment, I thought I smelled the scent of rain, but it was merely the collective perspiration that followed us down the church aisle and toward the open doors, where I could already see the columned remnants of clouds spreading away from each other, finding more importance elsewhere.

We all filed out, one by one like patrons at a theater, but I noticed that my mother and aunts remained behind. There were five of them, Rosa, Irene, Inez, Linda, and Gloria, and I found it strange that my uncles, Santiago, or Sonne as he was called, and the twins Javi and Jaime, were with my grandmother by the doorway, leaning over, explaining something with hand gestures I couldn't quite interpret. They looked somewhat agitated, even hurt, as though my grandmother had said or suggested something that brought up a past memory or event they didn't want to discuss given the current climate. It wasn't until I walked closer that I heard Sonne saying, "They don't have to do this. We can help, you know we can help. Por favor, Mom. They can't carry it all by themselves." He was both the oldest and tallest of the children, and because he stood about a foot and a half above my grandmother, I couldn't help but imagine her as some sort of queen next to a male head of state, conversing as they watched a military parade. Javi and Jaime were positioned in front of them, nodding along with Sonne's insistence on something that was happening inside the church.

"No. That is not what he wanted. Dijo. That's what he said."

"Ma," interjected Jaime, "Sonne is right. They can't carry it all by themselves." He looked around him, not noticing me, and tried to whisper, "It's too heavy. You know it is."

"I said no," she responded. "Your father wanted them to carry the casket. Las hijas. ¿Me entienden? He didn't want you to help. I told them that you all are not going to help."

Jaime stepped back, his body giving off this general sense of defeat. I would see him, along with Javi, working on his collection of low-riders all afternoon, drinking beers during barbecues before he was twenty-one, stabbing a butterfly knife in between his sprawled fingers on the backyard picnic table—increasing with speed after each round—and even that one time when he and Javi fought my stepfather in my grandparents' front lawn, pushing him back and forth, kicking him across the ribs, and shouting to leave my mother alone. But as he turned around, crossed his hands in the front of his black button-down—which fit him too large and awkwardly, especially since he wore an even blacker shirt underneath—he no longer carried himself with the confidence he had so often displayed, that I had so often admired, on a day-to-day basis.

"Why don't they let us, Mother, they will need our help," repeated Sonne. He too, despite the authority his height and size demanded, was at the mercy of my grandmother's insistence that my grandfather's will wouldn't allow the three boys to carry the casket.

"No," said my grandmother, wiping her cheeks with a folded piece of cloth. Sonne licked the bottom of his mustache, turned around, and placed both his hands on his bulging love handles.

"Okay," he said. "Fine by me. I'll just keep my mouth shut then."

As I studied my uncle, his long and disproportionate legs holding the larger, upper half of his body, the black boots and tight black corduroys I thought resembled those that men wore in mariachis, and that contemplative stare he inherited from my grandfather, I heard a large thud behind me. We all turned around, watching my aunts readjust themselves, shifting in unison to the side, and proceeding with their strides as they carried out the casket. Gloria and Inez were in front, Irene and Linda, the shortest and skinniest, in the middle, and my mother and Rosa were in the back. Although their positions seemed arbitrary, impromptu when they were inside the church ready to haul my grandfather out, I later learned that they had actually planned their positions about a week before, together going to the funeral home, testing out the casket, repositioning themselves so that strongest of the six took the corners, distributing the strength between them evenly.

The morning sunlight hit their faces, revealing women I didn't recognize completely, as though they had just aged about five or six years in the course of a few hours, had sprouted strands of gray hair, and had become complacent with their figures and what they wore, unconcerned with the holes in their black panty hose, the missing buttons on their blouses, the manner in which their eyebrow-tint veered slightly off the thin corners of their actual eyebrows. Their figures came into focus: six women carrying a shiny brown casket, six daughters who shared very little facial similarities with one another, who leaned their bodies to the side, gripped the casket's handle with each hand, stared at the hearse with their mascara-stained and Popeye-scrunched faces, ignoring my uncles and grandmother who stood looking on.

The wailing around us only grew, or at least I had heard it grow in a way I hadn't chosen to hear it before. The volume seemed to be increasing with each step the sisters took across the tiled squares of the church floor, with each labored tap of their high heels. I felt the crowd move closer to us. I saw my mother struggling in the back, releasing her left hand briefly so she could walk straighter, keep with her sister's stride. Jaime jolted toward them, reaching his arms in between my mother and Linda.

"No, please no. Muévate, Jaime. Please," my mother said. Jaime stepped back, clearly eager to say something. Linda turned her head around, confused with who was behind her, and nearly lost her grip. Jaime jumped back in and lifted the handle, and as if she knew just by the mere touch of his hands, Linda shouted, "No! Move! No!" Jaime pulled his hand away as though he had touched a stove grate he didn't know was on.

"Please," he said.

"No, Jaime," shouted Linda.

"And you too, Sonne and Javi! No!" shouted my mother.

Sonne and Javi had moved around to the other side, attempting to jump between Rosa, Irene, and Gloria. I couldn't see exactly what happened, but I assume that Rosa, in that stern attitude I feared every time she said she was going to throw a knife at my face if I didn't quit the habit of chewing with my mouth open, had slapped his hand away, and just by the look on Sonne's face, I could tell he wanted to slap her hand in return, call her something in Spanish I wouldn't understand, and insert himself where he thought he should have been. But instead, he backed away. Javi followed suit.

"I know it's heavy. Just please let us help you," pleaded Jaime. From my angle, it did look heavy, much heavier than it had during the viewing, when a large portrait of my grandfather stood next to it, and a kneeler was positioned in front, making its overall appearance seem lighter, like cardboard, like a styrofoam prop for high school plays. Average coffins weigh anywhere between one and three hundred pounds, or upwards to five hundred if the wood is thicker, longer in length. But that is mere material, and the casket is still an object that doesn't factor in the emotional and symbolic weight for each family, that never considered the way six daughters may feel when they are chosen in their father's will to carry the casket to the hearse, to momentarily forget the struggles they had with him growing up, how strictly they were raised: slapped for talking back, beaten when their teenage actions didn't align with the housewife roles he envisioned they would play. Casket makers didn't factor in how my grandfather would call my mother, the oldest daughter, a puta, a whore, a slut who wanted to go to college only to *fuck* and to *fuck around*, because *what the fuck could a college ever teach her that she really needed to know*, that my grandmother hadn't already taught her, that his demands hadn't already enforced? The hell with learning, the hell with gringo schools and institutions that sought to instill a Hispanic woman with the meaning of independence, the hell with such broad and clichéd concepts such as independence, the hell with concepts, the hell with thinking about concepts, the hell with thinking about thinking, and the hell with my mother's persistence. There weren't enough words or beatings to make her change her mind. She would disobey her father, go to college, move to Houston, be defiant, put two years of study under her belt, and move back to finish her undergraduate studies in social work at the local university. After graduating, she'd return once more to Houston, become a teacher, meet my father, have me, and then come back to the Valley to settle permanently when her marriage had failed and move into the house she was raised in, the house my grandfather built before building a new one next door. She would witness his deterioration, his blindness, how fragile he became, how much his skin, white-complexioned and wrinkled, had sagged around his face enough to look like some melted figure in a Salvador Dalí painting.

I saw it, too, but the indifference was only hers to harbor, to let fester, to finally release as an urgent stride that, while appearing to be a blend of mournfulness from the service and pain as the weight of the casket taxed her body, was really her desire to get rid of the symbolism all of this entailed. To no longer be the pallbearer she was chosen to be, chosen not because my grandfather had deemed her, along with her sisters, as the most dignified choice to carry him to the other side, whatever that other side consisted of, but more out of spite, a *Ha ha, I told you I'd have the last laugh* type of feeling I can now look back on and guess she was feeling as she lifted the casket higher, walked faster, grunted louder with each increasingly unsteady step.

"Move, Jaime, move," she said again, her breathing asthmatic. Jaime shook his head and backed away, embarrassed, irritated, yet clearly proud to have followed them all the way to the hearse, where they rested the front end on the bumper, straightened their backs, regained their postures, then lifted and shoved the casket in till half of it was secured—albeit awkwardly—on the gurney. Gloria stepped aside and flung her forearms on the tail light, while Irene walked off, placing her hands on her knees, as though she were about to vomit in front of the large water fountain where the hearse was parked. Inez, the youngest of the sisters, squatted and raised the middle section enough to see that it slid farther in. Linda had already let go, content with watching Rosa, Inez, and my mother do the rest of the work. My uncles were right behind them, stretching their arms, their spines, touching the back of the casket and pushing what they could inside.

Then, as I look on, Sonne begins to dissolve as the sunlight crosshatches his body. Next goes Javi, Jaime, my aunts mingling amongst the crowd, tilting their heads, wiping their tears, timidly looking back as the driver of the hearse, a short, somewhat heavyset man who just from the simplicity of his face, resembled my anonymous relatives, touched my mother on her shoulder, and nodded in condolence before closing one door, then the other.

I don't remember where exactly my grandmother was, but I figured she too had dissolved with the sunlight, had let the crowd embrace and escort her to the limousine as the new widow she was already beginning to embody in her solid-black dress. Time was no longer in anyone's grasp, and what could have been half an hour later, my grandmother reappeared at the cemetery, standing by the grave, watching her daughters carry the casket again. I stared at them, then at my grandmother for a few seconds, then at my mother and aunts who finally conceded some help to my uncles, allowed them to assist in pulling out the back end of the casket just enough for the sisters to reassume their positions. Then they each gripped their portion of the handle tightly, and again resumed their crying, their heavy strides through the lumpy grass between the tombstones, a space I was always reluctant to step on, somehow feeling that because the caskets were buried horizontally, I was stepping over them, disrespecting the memory of who they were, regardless of how deep they were interred below.

I noticed my cousin Eloy grazing the backside of the tombstones, as though he were tiptoeing a plank, while tapping the ribs of his older brother Ricky walking in front of him, nodding and urging that he move further from the center. Like muscle memory, I mimicked their movements, and so did my sister Iris and our cousins, Roy, Chris, Vanessa, Ivana, Eddie. They trailed behind me, and together we looked like some outcast group of children exploring the landscape of an uninhabited island, trudging through the exotic flora in a manner I found quite romantic, quite *Lord of the Flies*-esque. I moved without wanting to, and yet I didn't want to resist, didn't want to miss the tree-shaded figures of my mother and aunts as pallbearers with high heels that sunk further into the dew-speckled grass that caused them to twist their ankles, stop, check on each other with vocalizations that sounded primal, with stares only they could interpret, then continuing to move painfully, urgently, determinedly, until they were able to hoist the entire casket on the gurney that was set up just above the square hole.

Though I had expected the wailing to grow as the casket was lowered, it had in fact faded to a few faint sniffles and muddled utterances that mimicked those at the beginning of the church service. I wanted to cry, show sympathy in a very adult-like fashion, but didn't know how to, and when I place myself in these scenes again, I still can't feign any deeper sense of sorrow, and neither could my cousins, who like me, weren't crying, were barely lowering their heads as they stood in oversized button-downs, poorly ironed jeans, and black dressy shoes already dirtied by the pile of dirt I initially mistook for sand around the grave.

"Eloy, should we put dirt on it, too?" I asked, watching as one by one my grandmother, my mother, and my uncles and aunts took turns grabbing the shiniest shovel I had ever seen and tossing whatever they could scoop onto the casket.

"I don't know," he said. He leaned to his side and shrugged his shoulders. I remember that instead of his eyes I looked at his hair, the gel heavily clumped on the tips, the way the thin rows of strands, like the tilled rows of unemployed fields that composed much of the Valley, had strayed from the trajectory his comb had set out for them that morning, and had become wavy, hanging off the edge of his hairline like the metal teeth of some green tractor. He was thin, scrawny, perhaps underweight considering how far out his cheek bones protruded from his face, and he'd remain that way years later even after the minor growth spurt and the tattoos that were supposed to make him look bigger, tougher, more maturely developed, that unfinished Virgin of Guadalupe, the one of Jesus dying, on his ribs, the tear drops by his eyelids for his time spent in juvenile detention, the names of exes around his neck, his last name between his shoulder blades, his name on his knuckles, and that medley of gang signs that constellated his body. No, not even the Dickies clothing he wore—an outfit he sported because he was proud of being brown and from the barrio, and didn't mind the cliché that came with it, *cliché ni nada güey, I'd fuck up anyone irregardless of what they think of me*—could add enough weight to his bones to make him appear like he was no longer a teenager. But that wasn't him yet, and as he moved toward the grave I moved with him, already wondering how I would grab the shovel, where I would place my hands, and what I should feel after I tossed my clump of dirt.

Eloy and I neared closer, closer, looking up to see if any of these nameless relatives would stop us, knowing they wouldn't, because how could they, what right did they have to interrupt the somber and appropriate manner in which we were paying our respects to our grandfather? I wondered what they thought when they saw us get behind what we thought was the line and wait for the figure in front of us to finish with his share, if, when they were done, they would turn around and watch us dislodge the shovel from the ground, as if we would use up all the dirt, leave nothing for those still waiting their turn.

After we performed our duties, I grabbed my sister's hand and tugged her along as our cousins moved away from the crowd, unsure now where our parents were, and unable to distinguish who was who solely by their backs with everyone dressed the same: black on black. After some confusion, Ricky hurried us into the limousine that brought our mothers here, thinking that's where they would be. I learned some fifteen years later that since my uncles had taken the cars to the cemetery, my aunts had decided to go back with their husbands, while my mother, being the only divorced daughter, went with my grandmother. The limousine was scheduled to go back to the funeral home, but Ricky had instead instructed it to go to my grandmother's house, and the driver, who spoke very little English, agreed with "Si, yes, of course," and a nod. He did a U-turn and drove toward the cemetery's gates. We pressed our faces at the tinted windows, peered at the perfectly aligned rows of tombstones and shadows the trees casted melancholically over them. We turned our faces from the windows and no one moved. My eyes bounced between Eloy, Chris, Iris, Ivana, Eloy, Ricky, Eddie, Eloy, Iris, Vanessa, Eddie, Ivanna, then once more at Ricky, who said, "I think they saw us. I'm sure they saw us." We knew they hadn't, but remained silent, and as soon as Eloy found the controls for the windows and sunroof, we quickly strayed from the way we were supposed to act and began taking turns pushing the buttons, sticking our heads out, two, sometimes three at a time. I squeezed mine through as though there hadn't been a funeral, a ceremony, a church, a priest, a grandmother, eight uncles and aunts, and a mother who had forgot her only son and daughter at the cemetery, relieved to see the wind being kind to my face as the limousine pulled into my grandmother's house, where my mother and her sisters stood on the porch, surprised that their children were smiling, giggling, waving, and, from what I could tell, envious that we were so happy precisely because our minds were young enough to be so readily forgetful.

OF STEEL & BLOOD

All night, I've attempted to find a term for the fear of playgrounds. Backyard playgrounds. Park playgrounds. Schoolyard playgrounds. Abandoned playgrounds built in the middle of some rain-soaked, semi-empty neighborhood strangers find when they get lost in a city they've never visited before, wondering if the wide, corroded slides, the broken monkey bars, the seesaw with seats stripped of handles or padding, the graffitied merry-go-rounds overrun with knee-high weeds and grass, and the swing sets that sway regardless of whether there's wind or not, are indeed a symbol of a childhood ruined by urban neglect and circumstance.

The closest I came to finding what I sought was the word *traumatophobia*, the fear of injury. But a word for the fear of injury seems rather redundant since our bodies naturally fear pain. Then again, the fear of pain is *algophobia* and the fear of fear is *phobophobia*. But no, fear isn't the precise word I'm looking for, more like caution, an irrational sense of caution I have around playgrounds, around the memories they evoke every time I find myself near one, sweating on the basketball court, waiting for the next team to come on, only to momentarily stare at the playground sets just off to the side where a handful of children are swinging around the poles, weaving through the dome monkey bars, running between the swings and slides, climbing up the steel ladders, and moving swiftly from one metal platform to the next, caught in an intense exchange of a game they keep inventing as they play.

I'd often hit my shins on the edges of those platforms in elementary school whenever I'd attempt to outrun what I can now only remember as silhouetted, nameless boys I called friends, each of us pretending we were leopards, squirrels, Spiderman, or some mutant-like figure with the ability to scale the upper levels of the set in an agile yet hasty manner that always caused me to misjudge how high I could really jump, triggering a needle-like sensation that would spread between my knees and ankles, that would force me to stop, sit down and watch the bleeding from a thin, sometimes onion-white gash spill unpredictably to my scrunched tube socks, the blood like powder gliding down the screen in a broken Etch-a-Sketch.

Perhaps the word I need is *hemophobia*, the fear of blood, of being confronted with a fresh wound, a reopened scab. But blood—whether my own or from someone else—had never stirred such an extreme reaction from me on the playground because it wasn't the blood per se that I was concerned with, but more the mixture of it with the lumps of sand around the poles and slides which, like rain, puddled and ruined its consistency. I can extended my search to *eremikophobia*, the fear of sand, but now I'm merely mentioning phobias for the sake of word play, throwing out terms I studied only briefly, thinking that they could in some way help me understand how my caution of playgrounds stemmed from a memory whose narrative is as disjointed as its scenes are vivid, each paradoxical fragment slowly dissolving, blurring beneath the uncertainty rendered by the passage of time, until the borders of my recollected surroundings smudge like a cinematic dream sequence designed to give the audience a glimpse inside the hero's mind, his internal struggle.

Though I try to erase the blurriness, to give myself more clarity, the glaucoma remains, pulsing like rippled water, distorting the summer trees in the background, the baseball fields that hosted our little league games, the barbecue pits with men tending to the half-charred fajitas, sausages, and chicken, and their wives and children lunching on the picnic tables just behind them. On the day in question, the day I find myself trying to recapture in my memory, my mother had suggested a picnic to all five of her sisters who had gathered at my grandmother's house that weekend morning. Only my aunt Rosa found the idea exciting, commenting that this was a chance for all of us to get together in a setting less domestic, a place that didn't carry the memory of their dead father, and that allowed them the opportunity, no matter how brief, to immerse themselves in chisme, gossip.

I returned with my cousins Ricky, Eloy, and Eddie from Wal-Mart with white bread, packaged ham, Kraft cheese, pickles, Hot Cheetos, Doritos, two twelve packs of Coke, one twelve pack of Dr. Pepper (my aunt's personal favorite), a ten pound pack of ice, and medium-sized Styrofoam cooler whose handle seemed too flimsy to hold our soda, sandwiches, and snacks. My mother and aunt borrowed the half-used, perhaps expired bottles of mustard and mayonnaise from my grandmother's refrigerator, and all of us, standing together at the kitchen table, helped pour the ice into the cooler and pile the ingredients inside, while my other aunts, mingling in the living room, looked on with their disinterested stares.

The park, Harlon Block, was near the center of the city. It was named after a young marine who, along with five other servicemen, helped raise the American flag on Mount Suribachi in Iwo Jima. The Pulitzer-prize winning photograph, as well as the short film clip showing the men in action, is iconic, the epitome of what constitutes victory and patriotism in this country. But in Weslaco, he wasn't, and still isn't talked about much for some reason—or at least that's the impression I got when I'd mention his name to someone only to have the subject veer away from anything that pertained to history. I had only learned about him late in high school when my junior year history teacher mentioned who he was briefly during our section on World War II, but even he seemed indifferent to it, as though his achievement and service on that island didn't measure up to all the other events that were occurring across Europe and the Pacific. Whatever feelings people had toward the park's namesake, whatever they knew about him or didn't know, it appeared to my seven-year-old self that this was a place to be during the weekends, partly because there wasn't much to do in the city, and partly because people didn't have backyards big enough to host family gatherings or birthday parties that were occurring all around us as we stepped out of my mother's van and walked from one end of the park to the other, watching women hanging banners across their picnic tables, men hoisting piñatas from tree branches, each pony, Marvel superhero, and unidentifiable figure ready to be mangled by a sawed-off broomstick and the playful rage of a child who knows that the harder they hit, the more mini-chocolate bars, lollipops, and filler candies will gush out.

There was a water tower at one corner of the park and a hospital on the opposite end, where a shoulder-high, chain-link fence and a spotty line of trees divided the two. Besides the historic Cortez Hotel downtown, the hospital was the tallest building in Weslaco, and its mere stature and placement gave the park a greater sense of importance, as though it were vying to be the heart of the city.

They were seven of us in total: my three cousins, my aunt Rosa, my mother, my sister Iris, and me. We looked like biblical nomads crossing a desert, searching for another temporary place to call home. Already I was sweating, unsure why everyone else wasn't. Iris stayed close to me, pinching my shirttail, jumping in front then falling behind, then coming back to my side, skipping the whole way. She was excited, smiling, this was her first picnic, and she was ready to play with me and our older cousins, to be just like us boys, rough when the heat of things intensified during Cops and Robbers, Cowboys and Indians, a never-ending game of tag.

Iris was a year away from starting kindergarten, and although she had seen the playground sets in the elementary school I attended, would stare out the window when my mother dropped me off, they were small in comparison to those in Harlon Block.

"Do we get to play on it?" she asked me.

"Play on what?"

"That one," she pointed, "that playground? Can we play on it?"

"Yes, but after we eat," I said, trying to act like an older brother concerned his sister wouldn't understand that despite the casualness, picnics were done a certain way. There was an etiquette we had to follow for reasons I myself didn't know, and that I had hoped she wouldn't ask me to explain.

She ran up to my mother and helped her lift the rainbow-colored shopping tote full of haphazardly rolled towels and small blankets. For a moment, I though we're at the beach, that the shadows from the park signs are the lethargic shadows casted by beach umbrellas, that the light spurts of wind brushing our faces, like the backside of a parent's hand touching a sick child's cheek, were infused with salt, and that the sparrows and crows jumping from power-line to power-line, tree branch to tree branch were seagulls that would soon begin pestering us for the leftover portions of our chips and sandwiches, which my cousins, so apt to believe in urban myths, would entertain by wrapping a piece of bread around an Alka-Seltzer tablet, hoping that once digested, the seagulls would explode into a confetti of feathers, intestines, bones.

The sparrows and crows did indeed circle over us like seagulls, but my cousins—who any other time would have felt the need to, as Eloy would so often stated, *fuck shit up*, throw rocks at the birds the way they would at home, or take out their latest BB gun and shoot at their chests or heads from the open windowsill, pretending the neighborhood was a battlefield and they snipers—were too busy modifying our usual games to suit the playground, explaining that we could form teams for a hybrid version of tag that incorporated handguns, lasers, bazookas, and portals placed around the play structures, allowing us to easily escape our capturers and run to the objects we sanctified as *base*.

"I'm with Ricky," said Eddie. Because he was my age, there was a lingering sense that he had to compete with me, a mindset that became more aggressive when Rosa would make us stand with our backs against each other, see who was the tallest, or who ran the fastest, convincing us to initiate an impromptu race down the block and back. Eddie knew Ricky was quicker than all of us, and smarter too when it came to changing the rules of whatever game we found ourselves playing, working them to his advantage at the last second.

"Fine," said Eloy, grabbing my shirt sleeve and tugging me into his ribs. "It'll be me and Stevie. We're gonna beat you guys no matter what. Right, Stevie?"

"Yeah. Me and Eloy are the true champions," I said, puffing my chest out a bit, but in a manner not even I found intimidating.

Eddie sneered and tossed his head back; the spokes of sunlight poured over his olive face. Eloy lunged to his side and put Eddie in a headlock. "You're gonna be sucking my dick at the end of this," he said, laughing, pushing Eddie's head closer to his crotch. Eddie shook him off, and together they ran toward the playground set. Ricky and I ran after them, ignoring Rosa's comment that she was happy we were such good sons, that we were the kind of boys who didn't need to be asked to help their mothers.

We did a run-through throughout the playground set, jumping from platform to platform, swinging from the monkey bars, seeing who could make it across without stopping, or diving head-first down the slides, the hot metal searing our elbows, forearms, chins. The adrenaline numbed the friction, but of course I knew that when I got home, I would find random burns on my elbows, bruises around my knees and shins, dirt around my cuticles, and cuts on my palms and fingertips without fully knowing how I got them, forcing myself to remember what part of the playground set caused each, but being distracted with the feeling of contentment again when I remembered my cousins and I running to our parents, eating a sandwich with Doritos and Hot Cheetos stuffed in the middle, drinking Coke, a Dr. Pepper, answering *Yes* when Rosa and my mother asked if we were having fun, contesting them when they said we had to wait at least ten to fifteen minutes before we started playing again, explaining that no, this wasn't a pool, we weren't swimming, we promise, we promise we won't throw up, and darting back to the playground where we formed the teams we had shotgunned for that day.

Ricky and Eddie gathered by the monkey bars, while I stood with Eloy beneath one of the mesh platforms, listening as he concocted a plan that had me running around the outskirts of the set—the border where the sand meets the unwatered grass being *out*—and distract Eddie, since, as Eloy said so matter-of-factly, Ricky would want to go after him, continue their oldest and middle child rivalry. I wasn't sure how exactly the rules worked, none of us truly did, but two of us were *it* and the burden of being *it* was passed on only when both members of the team were tagged. And so we played, adding more rules, weapons, obstacles such as invisible walls and imaginary grenades that stunned the victim, just enough to run away.

"Stevie!" my mother shouted. She was standing on one side of the lowest platform, my aunt standing on the other. Iris was on top; her curled and tangled strands of hair sprawled against her forehead and temples, like rain-streaks on a car window. I was two levels up. Eddie was running somewhere below, finding it much easier to gang up on Eloy, who had extended the playing field to the green benches and tables all around us, running and rolling on each, yelling to his brothers that their hands had to touch his skin, not his shirttail or sleeves.

"Stevie!" shouted my mother again.

"What?" I answered, watching as Iris jumped into Rosa's arms.

"You need to let your sister play," my mother said.

"But it's only teams of two," I contested.

"You need to include her," she insisted.

"But Mom, it's only teams of two," I said, shrugging my shoulders, shaking my head. "Maybe when we finish."

"Esteban," said Rosa, placing Iris back on the platform. "Por favor, listen to your mom. She's your sister and you need to play with her. You understand? ¿Me entiendes?" Rosa's eyeliner had smudged, bleeding into her crow's feet.

Iris stopped and looked up at me, then smiled and ran to the edge of the platform. She hesitated and spread her arms out. "Jump, jump," said my mother, and Iris jumped, giggling, kneeing my mother's stomach. She was already having fun, I thought, why should she have to play with us? I wiped my brow with the collar of my shirt.

"After we're done with this round, Rosa. I promise, Iris will be on my team," I said, and before either of us could respond, I ran up to the next level and shot down the playground's tallest slide.

The early afternoon sunlight lacerated my face as I hit the sand, jolted and ran along the edge, where the sand meets the grass, unsure if my mother was looking at me or not. I didn't care if she was, I was more concerned with mocking Eddie so he would start running after me. My go-to lines for shit-talking were limited, constrained not only by a third-grade vocabulary—to which had already been added *shit, fuck,* and *dickhead,* words I used but only sparingly—but by the awareness that my mother was behind me, yelling something to my sister, so I stuck out my tongue, put my thumb on my nose and wiggled my fingers back and forth into a turkey face, and with my middle finger, I pretended to scratch my forehead and jaw, tempted to stick it farther out, to angle it sideways, make my gesture more threatening.

I was sure Eddie saw me, I was sure Ricky and Eloy did too, but when they cocked their heads suddenly in my direction, they looked past my faces. Naturally, I turned around and although the sound is still delayed every time I remember shifting my body, wondering what had stolen their attention from gestures they would have otherwise found funny, I could see the shock on the side of my mother's face, the same seriousness my aunt shifted into as she, a larger woman whose lower body had always been disproportionate to her upper half, moved around the platforms just as quickly as we all did, rushing over to my sister who laid face down in a pool of blood that grew larger, larger by the second. She lifted her head. Sand fell off, and for a moment I thought it was a part of her skin, as though the fall had rendered her body into sediment, debris. Her mouth was agape, bloodied like the paper plate full of red acrylic paint she would be dipping her fingers into during the arts and crafts section of kindergarten next year, somewhere between lunch, naptime, and phonics. Iris turned and more blood puddled out. I thought I saw small bubbles forming on the corners of her lips, each speckled with a constellation of sand. I thought she was trying to say something, maybe *help*, maybe *Mom*, maybe *God*, a concept she was beginning to understand, to ask me more about, questioning why He had chosen to cast himself in the sky, hide amongst the stars, why he didn't come down, get a closer view at a*ll the people he made*, call the moon his home. Yes, it was God she was muttering, I thought, how could it not be when I—still unfamiliar with the spiritual details of how God worked, what made Him intervene in some parts of the world, while others were left to find something that resembled divine intervention somewhere amongst the rubble and barrenness of their economically impoverished and natural disaster-inclined countries—had so often told her that God could see everything, knew what was happening every second of every day of every week of every month of every year of all time because by definition He was God and God created everything, had the power to fix things just as He had the power to destroy them. She bought it, at least some of it. I almost did too, and even if she, like me, would one day no longer find the use for God, gods, or any type of superficial spirituality that made one want to devote their lives to securing a spot for the life after, she tried to believe, quietly listening to the priest, climbing on top of my mother's lap for a better look at the altar, reciting prayers in Latin, in Spanish, in a simple English that was beginning to mold more firmly to her tongue.

Ricky ran past me, Eloy followed close behind. Eddie and I joined in last. We were hesitant to move in any closer, to lend our voices to the commotion, to squat over my sister, to stare at the blood curdled across the sand like jam scraped sloppily across a piece of burnt toast. Because memory has a way of flashing between scenes, as though the neurons were channel-surfing, looking for more compelling episodes, I can only make out a disjointed set of pictures and sounds, the incoherent cries and shouts, my mother's sweat-stained back as she throws herself down, Iris sprawled in her arms like a warzone child being carried off from a heap of bombed-out rubble, and her blood, as thick as it was unsympathetic, spilling from her mouth onto my mother's arms, so much that it appeared my mother was the one with the gash, that she had been bleeding for hours, her body unable to stop.

I felt lightheaded, like I had just stepped off of one of those pendulum rides at the carnival—the Pirate Ship, the Ali Baba, the Kamikaze. My chest tightened. My legs tensed. I looked around. The playground set became blurry, more than it already was, and within seconds I found myself moving, trotting behind my mother, my aunt, and Ricky and Eloy who were stretching a blanket out in front of them, Ricky shouting "Yes, it ends mom! Yes! The fence ends! We can go around it! We can go around it!" while Rosa shouted back, "Hurry, mijo! Hurry! Call them for help! Call! Run! Run!" Eloy dropped his end of the blanket and I sprinted over to lift it. I couldn't understand how my mother was moving so fast, how her near-diabetic legs were able to extend their stride, how it didn't seem as though she was breathing; her respiratory system suspended from its normal duties. She ran faster, rounded the gate and headed toward the hospital parking lot. The blanket slipped from my hands. My hands were bloody. I've committed a crime, I thought. I've hurt someone without even knowing it. My sister's head bobbled like the head of a plastic doll. But her pull-string was broken, and the only noise that came out was the noise of a three-year-old girl bawling, wailing, crying, fulfilling an entire list of synonyms for the manner in which our bodies easily express pain, suffering.

She flailed her arms against my mother's face, as though hugging her was all the comfort she needed. Bubbles rose in my stomach. My throat became warm. I was on the verge of throwing up, of pissing my pants, of going into shock, until I found myself, without knowing how, inside of a restroom, watching my chest expand, contract, expand, contract. I washed my hands of all the sand and blood. I looked up at the mirror, but no image was reflected back. I stepped outside and there were doctors passing by, nurses with clipboards in their hands, old, nightgowned patients sitting drowsily in wheelchairs just outside their curtained rooms, IV poles resting by their sides. Phones were ringing. Machines were clicking. The sound of rolling chairs added a rhythm that made the commotion almost bearable. I saw a hallway light flickering, another soul, I thought, attempting to cross to the other side, caught by the electrical set-up of a place that just upon first glance alone, looked like it was overdue for a renovation.

I spotted my mother at the end of the hall, standing with her arms crossed, listening as a doctor pointed to a room a few yards ahead of them where Iris rested on a gurney; her blood-dried head squeezed between blue rubber padding. I didn't have to be beside them to know that he was explaining how they would proceed, how they would run my sister through an X-ray machine, check if her neck had been fractured, examine her jaw, her teeth, see which ones were broken, and keep her overnight with enough medication to limit the pain she would experience for the next twenty-four hours. My mother mumbled something back. The doctor patted her on her shoulder, and just when I thought he was leaning in to hug her, embrace this mother who took her eyes off her daughter for a few seconds, unaware that she was climbing up onto a platform with a fire pole hanging off to the side, he pulled away, as though his sympathy couldn't see past the narrative of her carelessness.

My mother turned, looked but didn't wave me over, and as she went back to listening to the doctor, shaking her head, sobbing, I was quick to convince myself that any blame given after this whole incident was over, no matter how small, shouldn't be placed on me. I didn't lose sight of my sister. I wasn't present in those moments leading up to her fall. I had to be absolved, and the only way to feel that I was to not claim her as my responsibility, regardless of how things played out, how busted her lips were, how much blood she had lost, how much damage her front teeth had endured: her right, second incisor yellowed, dead, constantly reminding me for years to come of a day that she, despite my mother often retelling the story to us when we were older, wouldn't herself remember. And perhaps it was because I knew or sensed that she wouldn't remember that I went back into the waiting room with my cousins and aunt, unable to relate to Iris's pain, a feeling that now returns to me not so much as indifference, but as resentment of the fact that her memory doesn't retain the events the way mine does, that she has no qualms with parks or playgrounds, doesn't panic, doesn't flinch, doesn't think twice when one came into view on the side of the road, and wasn't spending her nights looking for a term that describes an anxiety she couldn't truly claim as her own, latching onto words that, together, only begin to scratch the periphery of fears that still lack a deeper meaning: *acrophobia, barophobia, odontophobia, megalophobia, metallophobia, nosocomephobia, iatrophobia, dsymorphophobia, symbolophobia, logophobia* . . . the list goes on.

ELEGY

The crow was dead, so we pushed open the office door and flung it in. It's June. No, July. It's warm enough to feel like summer, and that's the season I imagine when again this narrative demands a climate for the backdrop of a city whose mood is always lethargic.

There's a parking lot and a handful of cars that appear like post-apocalyptic props for a set in which all the scenes have already been filmed. There's a small, parched lawn with patches of weeds sprouting along the curb. There are trees with their trunks painted white, trees that give the impression they are imported from another country, trees whose serrated webs of shade become tangled with one another, forming labyrinths of shadows that together would embody something scenic if only a slight breeze would sweep in, give them movement.

The heat pulses around us, weighs down the branches, brands the metal poles I accidentally rub the sides of my elbows into, causing me to jerk back as I amble down the covered breezeway half lit by slanted streaks of sunlight. I look up and see the chiseled words WESLACO SCHOOL DISTRICT and the smaller words AD-MINISTRATION below it. Like me, my aunt is from Weslaco, and as far as my eight or nine-year-old self is capable of remembering, she had spent at least twenty some years of her life here before meeting my uncle and moving to the next town over, where my cousins Ivana, Junior, and Marcos go to school. Ivana's a Tiger. I'm a Panther, and though we are a good five or six years from high school, and there isn't any reason for us to take our rivalry seriously,

I feel as though her and my aunt shouldn't be here, that some-one will make her out, remember her from a football game, or the myriad of sporting events that bring our two towns together. I'm unsure if my aunt keeps up with high school football, but as I fol-low her, I assume that she does indeed go to games, that she wears the apparel, joins in the chants, watches them lose, and spends the rest of her Friday night with my uncle and cousins at a Pizza Hut discussing how next season will be better.

I study her as he walks in front of me: love handles, the light sweat and wet ponytail swaying between her shoulder blades, the tan line that separates her dark skin on the backside of her arms from her even darker flesh, I began to feel as though I'm the one who shouldn't been seen with them, who should keep my distance in case I'd ever have to defend any future accusations about my commitment to this city. As quickly, however, as this sense of be-trayal prompts me to hesitate, to look around and see if I spot anyone I know, my paranoia passes when a suited stranger passes by, ignoring all three of us completely.

The heat swells. The sky bruises. The sun pushes itself deeper into the breezeway. My aunt stops. I scrape the soles of my shoes against the pavement, notice that my shoelaces are a few steps away from becoming untied. I look up and see my aunt gazing at a piece of paper, mouthing a number that matches the number by the door. She turns, stares at Ivana and me, and tells us that she isn't going to take long. All she needs to do is submit her application. It'd be best if we stayed outside. We nod our heads. "Just don't go too far, okay? If you're gonna play anything, please do it right here. I don't want to come outside and see you guys on the street." She leans over, shifts her attention between Ivana and me. "Do you un-derstand?" she asks. We nod our heads once more. "Okay. Good." She stares down at the piece of paper again, turns around, opens the office door, and walks in.

The air-conditioning from inside unfurls far enough to touch my face. I inhale that office-scented mixture of gray carpet, fresh printer paper, faux leather, glossy desks. I exhale before the door closes, feeling like an actor in a breath mint or gum commercial. I open my eyes. Ivana smiles, exposing her crooked front teeth.

"It's hot," I say. I stretch the collar of my shirt, hoping the chilled air, like some sort of invisible ferret, would sneak its way in.

"Yeah," she says. "We should play something." She walks around me, grabs one of the poles, and with her right arm extended, swings around it two, maybe three times, then jumps onto the lawn and begins shuffling across the ground. Mushroom clouds of dirt flare around the socks scrunched down to her ankles. For a moment she looks like she is dancing. Before the dirt can acquaint itself with the earth again, she begins running, zigzagging back and forth and back in no particular pattern or direction. "We should play touch," she yells, or that's what I think she yells because playing tag was always the thing we did when bored.

I want to stretch this section of the story, say she's laughing, that she is spreading her arms out, mimicking an airplane, shuffling more dirt around her, and tagging me as I join in with the same attitude. But any attempt at describing the exact details of what happens next remains muddled in a realm between truth and fabrication, and although I'm sure that I do join her, run around, and swing from the poles just like she does, the scene again becomes blurry, and I must reimagine myself chasing Ivana in order to propel the plotline just enough to stop and find a lump of black bile laying by a tree.

I think it's a root, but as I walk closer, begin to give it shape, I think no, this tree isn't large or old enough to mirror those trees found in popup storybooks. I spot something fuzzy, perhaps a baby squirrel that has yet to learn the form and technique of jumping from one branch to the next. I crane my head forward, squat a few feet away and realize it's a crow. It's small, on its back, and its beak is open that same way death forces open the mouths of everything it claims.

Somewhere behind me I imagine Ivana is still running, yelling my name, explaining that tag only works with two players. But there is a dead crow in front of me, and I can't refrain from feeling it deserves my attention. I can't decide on its color. Its chest, or at least the part that's still intact, appears a shiny, fish-scale blue, while the feathers around its legs and wings are burnt charcoal tinged with streaks of gray. It has small, ulcer-like wounds around its neck, and blood is speckled around its belly. The mangled gap in its breast is curdled with lumps of a dark substance that has the same consistency as leftover cheese on a Little Ceasar's pizza box. There are flies hovering around it. There are maggots around the cavities, burrowing farther in. Their slow movements are almost cathartic, and I want to tell them that, explain in some maggot language how, despite my disgust at the sight of them, despite how they make me feel all gooseflesh and cold, I'm thankful that at least something has benefitted from this bird's death.

"Stevie," I hear Ivana saying, approaching heavily. "Ugh, what the hell?" She pulls back, hesitates, yet remains fascinated by the crow. "That's gross. What is it?"

"It's a crow," I say.

"It freaking smells," she says, pulling the collar of her turquoise shirt over her nose, which slips to her lips when she leans over, places her hands on her knees. "Is it dead?"

"Nah, it's just sleeping." Ivana shoves my shoulder. I lose my balance, but break my fall with my knuckles. I expect her to continue pushing me for the sarcasm, grab the hair in the back of my head, and yank it toward the dead crow, shouting *Of course I know it's dead! I'm not an idiot!* But instead, she pushes off my shoulder and squats on the opposite end of the fallen crow.

Ivana would grow up to be a nurse, marry in her early twenties, raise a boy, and live what could be considered a comfortable, suburban life in the same neighborhood that I would eventually move into. Our interactions, despite this proximity, would only happen at family gatherings and random sightings at Wal-Mart, convenience stores, and the bowling alley. But there is nothing here that foreshadows this when she begins lifting the crow's wings, examining the blood and lacerations beneath it.

"It looks like it was shot," she says.

"Maybe. I don't know."

"You go hunting with Tío Roy and Junior and Chris, right?"

"Yeah. Sometimes."

"Is this what it looks like when you shoot a bird?"

"We don't shoot crows."

"What do you shoot?"

"White-wings."

"That's still a bird, ain't it?"

"Yes, but . . . " I look up at Ivana, then back at the crow which, with its head angled to the side, I think could be listening, waiting for me to explain if it indeed was hunted or not.

"So . . . is this what it looks like when you shoot those White-wings?"

"Kinda. The shotgun shells have a lot of small BBs, so when you shoot it, it spreads out," I say, gesturing the action with my hands, "and only a few of the BBs catch them. It's not a large hole like this one." I point at the cavity, which appears to have been pierced with a bullet rather than a shell. But I know it's neither.

"What killed it then?" Ivana asks, and I immediately begin to think that this could be a pandemic, a new disease that infects birds first before mutating into a stronger, airborne strain that within days makes its way through the general population, causing our immune systems to weaken, our bodies to lose a large amount of weight, our scorched and cough-riddled throats to vomit pools upon pools of blood until we've become nothing but hairless, purpled, bruised, and bed-ridden skeletons leeching to life only through IVs, injections, and bedside predictions that claim a whole team of doctors and scientists are working on finding a cure.

I stand up, survey the parched landscape around me and think no, this is just my paranoia again, which again it is, and which doesn't die down immediately, but shifts into something more psychologically inexplicable, bringing to mind the movie *The Birds*, which I haven't yet seen in its entirety, but merely know through its most famous scenes: the crows gathering on the monkey bars, the crows attacking the students, the crows joining in with the gulls and sparrows in the final attack sequence, repeatedly pecking the face of the blonde lady until she can no longer hold them off—her limp body falling against the bedroom door, bloody and catatonic. This crow, the crow at my feet, is dead, and yet, these hypotheticals become my focal point, and I imagine the same crows I sometimes see perched on power-lines, gathering during autumn and chirping through the echo of city traffic below; that flock of silhouettes growing against a bruised slit of sunset and sky. They are not plotting against us, I remind myself, they don't want to peck out our eyes. This isn't a Hitchcock film, and although the scene has casted me as its main character, I assure myself that I am far from any such events.

"I don't know," I say. "It looks like it just fell from the tree."

"Maybe its wings were broken or something."

"Or it had worms," I add. "When animals are born they sometimes get worms in their stomachs. Sometimes they can live with them for a while, but other times the worms start to eat their intestines."

"Like with dogs, right?"

"Yes. Like dogs."

"Yeah, maybe that's what happened. It kinda looks like a baby." Ivana leans over closer and examines it. "I think it's a boy," she says.

"How do you know?"

"I don't know. It just looks like it." She shrugs her shoulders, then reaches over and with her index finger and thumb, begins touching its beak. She opens it and with a voice that sounds as though she had taken a balloon full of helium, says, "Do you want to play with me, Stevie?" Half of me wants to laugh, but the other wants to push her face against the wound, make her eat the maggots for being so callous with the body of a dead animal. "Do you, Stevie? I want to play with you."

"I— I— ," I stutter, badly muffling my laughter.

"I want to be loved," she says. "I want to be loved."

Part of me did, in fact, want to love it, the same way that part of me wanted to love both my stepfather and grandfather even more after they died. But I couldn't, not because I couldn't feign the feeling of love, but because I saw no point in feigning it, in thinking that things must be done out of respect for the way they were once done before. Plus, this is a crow, and in the long list of things people should be grieving for, crows are near the bottom, just below oil-covered seabirds struggling to rid themselves from an accidental spill.

"Stevie, love me," says Ivana, now using both hands to manipulate its beak.

"Stop it," I say.

Ivana cackled her signature cackle, a sound I'd try to hide from every time I went to the movies with her and my aunt. I tune her out for a moment, and just as I think she's about to lay the head to rest, leave it be, and continue urging me to play tag, she grabs the crow's legs and hoists its body just above the ground.

Because I was raised to believe that even the simplest things can be religious, I think of an upside-down crucifixion, what I imagine would be punishment for a rebellious angel, but on a smaller scale.

"What are you doing?" I ask. Her face is serious, eyebrows slanted against each other like a cartoon character. Ivana doesn't respond. "Why are you picking it up?" I ask again. "It could have like rabies or something."

"Rabies are for dogs," she says.

"I said *like* rabies."

"We should throw it on the pavement, so when people walk by, they get all scared and stuff."

"Huh?"

"Yes, let's throw it." She smiles, hoists the crow in front of her. The flies faithfully follow it. Dirt and grass fall from its back. I walk closer, certain that she's only playing.

"Why would we do that?"

"Why not?" she says, tiptoeing toward the breezeway, as though she were playing a game of Don't Touch the Lava.

"Let's just put it right here, okay?" I follow her, also finding myself tiptoeing. "Are you really gonna throw it there?"

"Yeah," says Ivana, stepping onto the concrete. I hear a car passing but don't turn around. I tiptoe quicker and as I inch up behind Ivana, watch her stop, I look around her and see how long the breezeway is, how many offices there are, how many people were probably inside.

What were they doing here? What were we doing here? Ivana lifts the crow, its head swaying like a wind chime. Then she drops it. There's a thump when it hits the pavement. Its neck snaps back. A few feathers come off. The wounds wiggle like expired Jell-O, and a few maggots spill out. Ivana laughs, then steps around it, runs a few yards down the breezeway, and looks back.

"You stay on that side, okay? So we can wait and see if someone finds it." Before I can respond, I find that I'm backpedaling, doing as I'm told. Ivana lets out another cackle as she runs farther down. I lean against one of the poles and study the lump of flesh and bone. It looks like a nest. It looks like a rag on the road. It looks like a shredded piece of a bicycle tire. It looks like used barbecue coal. It looks like I am in need of better similes, none of which I'm able to construct at the time, knowing, however, that there's no need for language to go beyond any simple description of a dead crow because people would have no trouble recognizing a dead crow when they step out of their offices, study it, jolt back in disgust, and call the custodial staff to clean the mess up.

I linger by the poles for a few minutes, try hard not to stare too long. No one comes out. A car passes on the street, then another. There's a neighborhood constellated around these offices, the old side of the city where the houses resemble shacks, old sheds, or small barn houses that with the heat, grow into something of a shantytown, or those *colonias* that could be found farther north of the city, areas where roads, clean water, and local ordinances were limited. Ivana appears frustrated, too. She walks up to a door and presses the side of her face against it, listening, listening. She moves her head back and comes running to me, sidestepping the crow. I meet her halfway.

"What?" I say.

"I don't even know if anyone's there."

"Your mom went into that one," I mumble, pointing at the door in the middle.

"Maybe not all of them are being used," she says.

"Why don't we open one."

"A door?" I ask.

"Yeah, and let's throw it in," she says.

"Throw it in?"

"Yes. We open the door and throw it inside."

"But there are people in there."

"We just have to run away. Really fast," she answers.

"I don't know. I think they'll catch us," I say, unconvincingly.

"Come on. We'll scare them."

I want to counter her enthusiasm, say it's too risky. But then again, tossing a crow can be fun, rebellious, out of the ordinary, utterly strange and bold.

"Are you sure?" I ask.

"Yes. Let's go." She turns around and heads toward the crow. I follow. "You grab that end," she instructs, pointing at the left wing, "and I'll grab this one. I'll open the door and then we both throw it in."

"How far?"

"As far as we can," she says, her gums partly exposed. "Got it?"

"Yes," I say, suddenly finding myself laughing, looking down at the crow and not seeing it was a once-living creature, but an object that no longer has value, that can easily be tossed into an office building for the sake of tossing it, and for the chance to later tell our friends and cousins what we did.

I reach down and smell the rot festering. The maggots, however, have disappeared, or perhaps they were never there to begin with, something I invented to emphasize the crow's decomposition. I close and open my eyes, and they come back. I shake my head and grab its wing with my right hand. Ivana grabs the other one. "Tickle, tickle," she says, flickering her fingers against its feathers. I look around; still no one. Slowly, we carry the crow to the nearest door.

"Was this the one your mom went into?" I ask.

"I dunno. Open the door. Go."

"I can't open it. I'm a righty." I expect some push back from her, some explanation that since it was her idea, I needed to complete the other half of the work. She gives me a look. I feel I should add something, defend myself, say I'm not a sissy, just at a disadvantage given the way I'm postured, and the fact that it would be inconvenient of me to reach over with my left hand with the crow still in my right. But Ivana lets go of her end and uses her entire body weight to yank open the door.

With the crow now swinging in my hand, I have no choice but to throw it. I watch it fly into the office, plop in the middle of the carpet. There are people inside, but no one immediately moves, and at least a good five seconds pass before a lady, tucked away in the corner where I can't see, shouts. From what I can tell, she jolts out of her chair. In front of me, I see a bald man jump from his desk. "Whoa!" he shouts. I watch him watch the crow. I can tell he is wondering if it's a real crow or just a toy of sorts, a plush black ball for dogs. He is tall, husky, has a goatee, large hands, and beneath his light purple long-sleeves, I envision a sleeve of tattoos, a cross here, a skull there. He pushes his chair back, almost kicks it, and jumps around his desk, heading for the door. Ivana lets the door go and runs down the walkway. I stare at the man, then the crow, then the man, the crow, the man, the crow, and as he moves around the crow, like a soccer player moving around a ball he intends to pass rather than take possession of, my reaction takes hold, prompting me to turn and run, to swing my arms the way Robocop does—my flat palms cutting awkwardly through the air.

"Hey!" I hear him scream. I am focused on the parking lot, where Ivana, whose ponytail I think of as a propeller giving her an extra boost, is close to entering. "Hey!" he shouts again. My legs pick up speed. I look down to find shoelaces untied, each pair scraping the pavement like tin cans on the back of wedding cars. The man shouts once more, this time louder, bolder, and because it echoes with more authority than I expect, my body stops. I don't want my feet to slow down, to quit running in the middle of the breezeway and pivot back where they came from, but they do, as I, feeling what I still can't tease out as a sense of guilt, stop, turn around, and slowly head toward the door.

Beads of sweat collect along my eyelids, clouding the man and surrounding offices. I look down, measure my steps, catch my breath. I flip through a range of excuses. *It was an accident. We thought there was no one inside. We thought it was still alive and just wanted to get it to some place cooler.* But then I'm in front of the man, looking up, unable to reply to his questions. My adrenaline crosshatches his face, that anger and disbelief that I would both throw the crow inside the office and that I would then fail to follow his demands to pick it up. He points inside, while a lady, perhaps the one I had imagined jumping from her chair, holds the door open.

I walk in and note the change in temperature, the atmosphere that resembles the same feeling of importance one gets when they walk into a bank. There are about three or four people huddled between the desks. There are calendars hanging from the walls, some with the days marked off, some with pictures of students on the top half, as well as portraits of what appear to be school board members, each smiling, angled professionally for the camera. And there is the crow at my feet, its neck and head craned back like the fossilized remains of velociraptors. It looks calm, as though it had found a place it could peacefully decompose in, and beautiful in a way taxidermy looks beautiful for a moment. I know I shouldn't move it, that I should run out, slip through the man's hands, meet Ivana in the parking lot, and wait till my aunt finishes whatever business brought us here in the first place. I lean over and place my fingers beneath it. It feels mushy, like backyard mud one mistakes for solid ground when they first step on it, and despite the minute or so spent inside this air conditioned office, the body is still warm, perhaps even more so than it was before I threw it in.

I know she won't, but hope Ivana comes in at any second and confesses that she took part in this event, maybe even take the blame because she is, after all, two months older than me, and trouble of this kind follows a hierarchy of age. But when I tighten my grip around the crow and turn around, only the man is standing by the door. The hum in my ears intensifies to the point that I think I'm about to faint. I carry the crow like I would a plateful of hot food, and as I study it, watch the maggots reappear from its rib cage, I realize that I'm already at the tree, laying it down and kicking dirt over its wings.

My aunt is going to come out. I feel it. I wipe my hands on

my shorts and backpedal. Frame by frame, I'm growing smaller, nearly gliding the farther I pull away from the crow. The scene is now focused on the back of my head, on my dark brown hair, on my shoulders postured like a mannequin's, on the blue-and-orange striped polo I remember my mother buying at Wal-Mart against my every protest that I wanted a shirt without a collar. Enlarge the image once more, and you can see me moving farther back, watching myself watching the crow lose its tropes as a clever, creepy, thieving bird, lose those metaphors and motifs that despite my attempt to understand, I know I'll have to return to years later to reinterpret.

RAPTORS

I lost two of them.

The first was a clay figure I sculpted out of Play-Doh in second grade for a science fair project. Our assignment was to develop a visual model demonstrating one of the competing theories surrounding the extinction of dinosaurs, researching the impact and force behind a six-mile wide asteroid, the indiscriminate contagiousness of a new disease infecting the tiniest to the largest bodies equally, the devastation of a sudden famine, of accidental inbreeding, of a volatile, super volcano whose eruption vomited so much lava it enveloped the planet in a fiery coat that redefined the habitability of a landscape that, some sixty-five million years later, would host our earliest ancestors. The class was divided into groups of four. Ours had three boys, one girl. Although the boys' names have long since escaped me, and now reside somewhere between Adrian, Adan, and Andrew, I remember the girl's name was Christian. She was tall, skinny, symmetrically proportioned with bushy eyebrows that suited her hazel-complexioned face and that complemented the variation of long, floral-patterned dresses she wore every other day. She was a girl who, if she had not gotten lost in the yearly shuffle of redistricting, I would have fallen for in high school, been, as my friends and I liked to say when we found ourselves strongly drawn to the opposite sex, *mad-crushing on,* both because of the simplicity of her attire and the complexity of her personality. I suspect she might likewise have gravitated towards me, finding a bit of enjoyment every time she led me on, broke my heart again, again.

As the self-selected leader, Christiane had given herself the responsibility of making the volcano. To our collective surprise—when, a day or two before our project was due, she brought to school what she had so far completed—the volcano came out better than we had expected: a foot long by foot wide model she had framed with chicken wire glued to a circular Styrofoam base, wrapped in paper-mâché, and painted with dark brown acrylic she concocted by mixing yellow, green, red, black and blue all into one. It was placed in the corner of our tri-fold poster board, while the paper lava that resembled Hot Cheetos crumbs poured toward the center, overtaking a color-penciled river, trees made from popsicle sticks, cotton ball bushes spray painted brown, and critters we had drawn to give our environment a more authentic look.

Christian's craft, I had to admit—not out of any sense of jealousy, since our portions of the project were distinctly different—was good. Thorough, appropriately sized for the board we were working with, and menacing for the onlooker, as it should have been, evoking what we had hoped would be a distinct disease upon realizing that such a thing once existed, that in the final moments leading up to the mass extinction, it spat out ashen columns of smoke and gurgled a steady flow of lava that killed and fossilized the creature I loved the most.

I made my velociraptor from clay, or rather, from bottle after bottle of Play-Doh I had borrowed from our teacher, Mr. Mac, and that I insisted my mother buy, nagging her at Wal-Mart, Kmart, whatever mart or market we found ourselves in, tugging on her sleeves and elbows, guiding her toward the arts and crafts department in the back. My mother conceded, although reluctantly, considering I had a bad habit of putting Play-Doh in my hair at night, wrapping it tightly on the top of my head, weaving it between the strands, and spreading it to my scalp, only to see if I could take it off in the morning, yank the hardened clump of putty in one attempt. There were times throughout my elementary years when the Play-Doh had cemented to the follicles, wouldn't budge, and my mother, faced with the dilemma no child-rearing book or familial advice could assist with on, would snip off those affected locks, leaving me with a constellation of bald spots that made it seem as though she were giving me the liberty to cut my own hair.

But, for my velociraptor, I abstained from all hair-driven Play-Doh urges. I needed every piece in those bottles. This was personal, this was intimate, this was a chance for me to create the raptor I had read about in textbooks, studied in class, seen in *Jurassic Park*. The kind of raptor I pretended I, myself, was, every chance I got. To get into character, I'd fold my pinky finger and thumb and stick the remaining three fingers out. Then, with my knees bent, my back slightly hunched, and my face contorted in the best raptor impression I could make—forming my lips into a snout—I'd roam around the house terrorizing inanimate objects, TV sets, couches, kitchen appliances, tables, chairs, dishes, cabinets, opening every drawer and bumping into the walls because I was a raptor and raptors didn't give a shit what was or wasn't around them, they did what they wanted. After I rearranged the household, avoiding, circling, or running past my mother, I'd move on to my sister, who, although occasionally convinced to embody a triceratops—lock her imaginary horns in my stomach, jaw—generally wanted nothing to do with my more aggressive behavior.

For me, the transition was easy. Watching the VHS of *Jurassic Park* on repeat had given me all I needed to become a self-proclaimed expert on dinosaurs, and like any impressionable second grader, I perfected my imitation the more I practiced, tying my shoes with three fingers, responding *rwrapp, rwrapp* when my mother would ask me clean up the kitchen, throw out the trash, organize my room. *I'm a raptor, I'm the raptor. Rwrapp, rwrapp* I repeated to myself as I began working on my part of the project, sculpting an outline of its body with my palms, forming its legs and tail with my fingertips, and detailing its facial features—eyes, teeth, nose—with the bent end of a paperclip. For two weeks, I went to the underfunded space we called our library and checked out additional textbooks so I could better understand the raptors' movements, proportion my model's limbs appropriately, and angle its neck in such a way that it looked like it was aware of the volcano behind it. I wanted it to be intelligent, cunning like the raptors on screen, stealthy and committed to the ruthlessness that made these creatures so alluring.

What I didn't take into consideration, however, was the size of my raptor in relation to the volcano. And when Christian and I brought our pieces together, our prehistoric scene looked exactly like a scene created by children whose bearing on measurements wasn't precise or developed. *I fucked up*, I remembered thinking, familiar with the words my mother smuggled from my aunts beneath her tongue. *We're going to lose*. The judges will mark that as the first mistake, and then be picky about the Hot Cheetos lava, the penciled critters, the bushes that were beginning to lose their commitment to the board.

When it came time for the contest, the judges asked questions, we answered, explained what the theory had going for it, where its shortcomings landed. But a few days after the event, Mr. Mac gave us the news, in his enthusiastic, *finally-I-taught-these-kids-something* fashion, that we got first place in our class, commenting not only on our project's artistic angle, but also on the information we provided, the concise, factual, and well-cited details which, unbeknownst to him, were correct thanks to the late-night assistance from our mothers.

Although he was in his thirties, Mr. Mac only had a few years of teaching under his belt. He wanted to like us, to like his profession, but his partially untucked shirt, his short temper, his lack of family portraits on his desk, and that one, maybe two rapidly taped student drawings on his wall said he had no intention of staying long. Nevertheless, he spoke like a teacher that day, and he stood like one at the front of the classroom, explaining that we not only did a great job but that tomorrow we were going to have a lottery to raffle off our models to one student in our groups. I leaned forward in my chair, listening for any specifics regarding how exactly the lottery would be carried out: a name drawn from a hat, a ticket selected at random, a bingo hall device with a number corresponding to the number we chose at the start of class. I was confused, uncertain why Mr. Mac was making this into an event when it could have been easily settled amongst our group, civilly worked out between what I assumed were a class full of civil second graders. He gave no indication of this, however, moved onto the lesson, and as he drew something on the whiteboard, my body became feverish, heavy, and I grew increasingly annoyed that we were being cheated out of all the hard work we had done. Christian could have taken her volcano. Adrian or Adan or Andrew could have taken their goddamn bushes, drawn rivers, and poster board. I wanted my raptor, and I felt in my gut that Mr. Mac knew it, too, he understood my fascination with the creature, perhaps seeing me as a reflection of himself when he was younger, more prone to obsessing over certain things, no matter how strange others thought they were. But as a teacher, the idea of fairness to all of his students superseded any hint of sympathy I thought I heard in his voice when he turned and looked at me and announced that precisely because the projects were so good, the best way to keep each intact was by allowing only one student to take it home.

That evening, I slept before being told to do so, eager to wake up early and be the first one in class, thinking that Mr. Mac would excuse himself of all the fairness bullshit and play favorites, maybe drop an extra slip with my name written on it into the baseball cap resting on his desk. In the morning, the slanted specks of sunlight streaked shyly through the window curtain, as though the sun, already burdened with its daily responsibility, were somehow aware and sensitive that as I yawned awake, moved my arms and legs, I'd find my neck unable to unlock from its position. I twitched. A sharp pain shot from the left side of my neck down to the inside of my shoulder blade and to the middle of my spine. Then it shot back up, then down again, prompting the left side of my body to spasm. In second grade, I'd sometimes still sleep with my mother, not yet adjusted for the darkness of a bedroom with wood paneling, uneven linoleum floor, houseflies that buzzed and crawled across the window mesh, trying to escape that which—with a shoulder-high dresser whose flimsy shadow resembled, depending on how the neighbor's fluorescent outside light shone in through the window—either an old, hunched-over man with a storybook cane or a lady in a black dress that gave her demeanor the impression that she had more malicious intentions. There was a thick brown blanket that divided my room from my mother's which, if I'd let myself be intimidated by its unwashed scent, its bleakness, the way it seemed to be darker than the darkness clinging, moth-like, to the unpainted drywall, I'd think of as a hospital curtain sectioning off what was so easy to consider the illness of my mother's nightmares, the undiagnosed reasons why she'd moan and ramble in her sleep, then suddenly shout for that reoccurring, anthropomorphized cat to get off of her throat, because no, she didn't do it, *Please, I didn't do nothing, stop scratching me, stop it, stop it, stop it, please!* The way she'd describe the cat—its lemon-green eyes, its quickness, how it wasn't a solid entity, but more a specter that could move in and out of the fuzzy atmosphere around her—it sounded like something from a *Goosebumps* novel, which even my seven-year old self found ridiculous, invented, exaggerated in much the same way that my friends and acquaintances perhaps now think of my dreams when I explain how every one of them revolves, in some shape or form, around my teeth sliding out, each rotted, yellowed, deformed and crookedly sprouting from my melted gums clumping along my cracked, enlarged lips; my mouth and jaw as disproportionate as one of Picasso's mistress portraits, but without the color to give it artistic value, meaning. My sister, only three at the time, slept in a small bed off to the side, near the other curtain that divided my mother's room with the living room. But to my memory, Iris never woke up during these episodes, never heard our mother's screaming for this imaginary cat to stop.

I heard the bathroom sink running. I figured my mother was in there with my sister, brushing her teeth, dressing her for daycare. I shouted something incoherent, perhaps their names, perhaps my own. The restroom door—a peeling, beige-painted wooden door I would draw stick figures, bad renditions of the Titanic, and two-dimensional landscapes on—jerked open, and after a few seconds, my mother came in with my sister tailing her side. She asked the standard motherly questions: *What's wrong? What hurts? Where? How bad? On a scale of one to ten, how high does the pain go?* And there was the overdramatic shouts and whines on my end, that claustrophobic feeling that my neck would never unlock from its position and I would spend the rest of my life looking to my left, walking like a crab and watching the world from a skewed perspective.

If only I had slept right, I thought, if only I had the foresight to predict that something like this would happen. I moved and down shot the pain again. I squirmed in my mother's bed, punching the pillows, kicking the headboard, gripping the nightly shadows that were still sprawled across the sheets. I began crying, began thinking about my raptor, began resenting my mother for having slept better than I did, for not waking up with the condition that I would discover as torticollis (wry neck, head tilt), a lingering numbness that would take it's time to subside, releasing me from its hold in the evening when again I'd sleep early, excited and hopeful that in the grand cosmic scheme of trivialities such as this one, the one and forth odds that my name would be called during that lottery would work out in my favor.

It turned out the universe was playing sides. Mr. Mac smiled when I entered the classroom the next morning, asking how I was, if I still felt sick, if I visited the doctor's office or took any medication, Tylenol and tomato soup always worked for him. My classmates filed in, we picked up our breakfast, small talk about *WrestleMania* flared up, as well as elbow drops on the desks and head locks on phantom bodies, and immediately after the first period bell rang, Mr. Mac announced to the whole class that he was glad I could join them today, that he hoped I felt better, and that he was sorry I couldn't make it yesterday since I was chosen to take the project home. I tried not to smile. I half-squatted in my seat, about to stand up when the *but* slipped from his mouth, that sudden change in tone, that slight pause and hesitation clogging the speaker's throat when they realize the next words they utter must constitute a legitimate excuse, that dagger to the heart of my ears whenever my mother would tell me in the middle of the toy aisle, *You know I never say no when we can afford it.*

Mr. Mac stood up, put his hands in his pockets and looked down at the floor. "But unfortunately, since you weren't here, I felt it wouldn't be fair to the rest of your group members, so we raffled it again and Christian was chosen to take the project. I'm sorry. Your velociraptor was awesome. Next time." I sat back down and followed Mr. Mac's instructions, pulling out some folder from my Spiderman backpack. My neck became stiff again, this time because of embarrassment. My classmates weren't laughing, didn't even notice how red I felt myself becoming, how tightly my muscles tensed, how desperately I wanted to be back in my mother's bed, especially after my body eased out of its tension for a moment and I looked up at Christian—our desks still in groups of four—unsure how I felt about the quick smile she gave me, as though it was meant as a consolation, or the confidence she displayed as she raised her hand, answered a question, looking beautiful in a way I had never noticed before, how her slender face remained concentrated on the board, how she finger-flipped her partially uncombed hair that hung off her shoulder in some mermaid, folkloric fashion, perhaps aware that as I continued to stare, suspending any attempt at subtlety, I'd do nothing but merely look on, feeling as wronged as any jealous creator.

I lost the second soon after.

A decade after the release of *Jurassic Park*, I learned velociraptors weren't those reptilian, scale-skinned creatures featured on film, but animals with their bodies covered in feathers, each the size of a small turkey, weighing no more than thirty pounds, give or take. They didn't travel in packs. They weren't intelligent in the same cunning fashion as they were on screen, using tools to their advantage, vocalizing the location of a potential prey. And despite their name, which roughly translates to *swift thief*, they were suppressed by their anatomies, and would today not be able to outrun the most mediocre of athletes.

Velociraptor mongoliensis lived during the late Cretaceous Period, after the Jurassic Period, and only a dozen or so fossils remain. I'd like to think that after I discovered these facts, read that the producers of *Jurassic Park* took liberties with the raptors, made them bigger, more agile, shaped them into a truly authentic American villain, I would no longer feel enthused about the dinosaur I once obsessed over, that it would result in a kind of shock and trauma that would make me wary of anything paleontological, that the image I had of it would lose its childhood significance, get demoted as that necessary evil I found it to be in the dinosaur kingdom. Although I felt chided by Steven Spielberg, wanted to punch him in the face or at least ask why he would give his audience the impression that raptors were a lot more intimidating and intense than the small, feathery creatures they actually were (only *Utharaptor ostrommaysorum*, a larger theropod belonging to the same family *Dromaeosauridae* could lay its claim as being the closest to the raptor we envision when the name comes to mind), the feeling subsided after a few minutes, and I knew that even as child keen to attain only accurate information, I would have overlooked these details and focused on the larger picture, the fact that it was still a carnivore, that the large, sickle-shaped claw on its leg was used to tear and restrain its prey, that its overall structure remained the same (albeit on a smaller scale), and that it would still have been attractive to me in those days, enough to continue drawing them throughout the third and fourth grade, producing sheet after sheet of velociraptors angled in different directions, facing every which way.

The first sketches were rough, two-dimensional, uneven, as though they were being seen through a magnifying glass. There was nothing about them that seemed real. The eyes were always too wide, the arms too long, the abnormal claws on the raptor's legs too lopsided and sharp, the mouth too open, too intentionally menacing. When I would take a break and look at it closely, examine the smudged scales, spots, and old battle scars I had painstakingly labored over for hours, I'd realize it really didn't seem menacing at all. I would pin these drawings to my walls, make sets, put the new ones above the dresser, stuff the old ones in a sketchbook beneath my bed, while a half-complete drawing clipped to a clipboard rested on the floor where, after getting dressed in the morning, I'd put in a few strokes before school, and finish another part of its body—tail, neck, arms—when I got home.

My mother bought me dinosaur books, some with cartoon drawings, some with pictures of models, others with an unnecessary number of words and captions, the text wrapped around a pack of curious raptors. And toward the end of each, there was an extinction event, an erupting volcano, a widespread famine, a cluster of asteroids hailing from the heavens, hitting the ocean in the same apocalyptic manner I'd always find in the brochures Jehovah's Witnesses would occasionally leave at our house. I remember one morning opening the door to a pair of older women dressed in black and maroon skirts, their hair still wet, or glazed with enough hair spray to give it that fresh-out-of-the-shower look.

"Buenos días mijo, ¿estan tus padres?" I knew what the woman on the right had asked for, but my tongue wasn't familiar with responding to questions in Spanish with Spanish.

"Yes," I said reluctantly. I stood still, trying to make respectable eye contact, studying the worn Bibles they held across their chest like clichéd schoolgirls, their short black purses that appeared to be empty. They were short, slender women with belly fat that nonetheless lumped over their skirt seams, with skin like pottery, skin that resembled my grandmother's, callused with the memory of a migrant sun.

The woman on the right looked at the one on the left, then at me, and in a broken, somewhat decent English said, "We are from the church down the street and we wanted to give this to you and your family." She handed me a brochure, the title in the front said *Testigos de Jehová*, and there was a question beneath, perhaps asking if I was ready for the return of Christ, or if I had ever considered seeking redemption for my sins. I opened it, acted interested, aware from my mother and aunts that people who went from door to door were Jehovah's Witnesses, and we were supposed to avoid them precisely because they weren't Catholics, some rift between the denominations I didn't quite understand. Toward the end of the brochure, there was a line of people—family members, most likely, given their physical similarities and how happy they were to be holding hands—walking toward a light that went beyond the page. In the background, there was an exploding building, smoke billowing from the roof like the sugarcane fires I'd see when I'd go hunting for white wings with my uncle and cousins in the backcountry. Why were these people smiling, I asked myself, why weren't they helping whatever workers or patrons I assumed were slowly dying in that building? I flipped the brochure to the last page, and there were people seated on a rolling expanse of green hills, eating fruit, walking by the edge of the cleanest and clearest lake I had ever seen rendered on paper.

Everything was perfect, and how could it not be in paradise, a concept I had trouble accepting even at an early age, not only because I realized how boring it would be to sing, praise, and offer eternal love to a god who never seemed above petty jealousy, but because the idea of something lasting forever seemed too far-fetched, which is why I'd question my CCD teacher, who also happened to be my aunt, when we'd discuss heaven, or especially Genesis, another lesson on creation, the whole nine yards of seven days, Adam and Eve, animals in the Garden of Eden (none of which included dinosaurs, no brontosaurus, no t-rex, no triceratops, no goddamn raptors), I'd remember thinking when my aunt said I had to read between the lines, that the word *dinosaur* was a term invented only within the past two hundred years (the Bible being over three thousand), and that, unlike those Protestants, Pentecostals, Presbyterians, and whatever other denomination beginning with the letter P, Catholicism actually accepted the theory of evolution, seeing no problem with the teaching it promoted for centuries.

It's always been part of God's will, I can still hear her say.

I wasn't satisfied. *In between the lines* was a cop-out, saying that the men who wrote the bible had a different terminology we modern sinners can only hope to spend our entire lives understanding was merely silencing any doubt about the infallibility of that ancient, selective document. My aunt and I verbally sparred during the ten minutes of question time she'd reserve toward the end of class: her attacking my youth, claiming I wasn't versed enough in dinosaurs to see how they played within the larger scheme of biblical history, while I went after her inability to explain her side of the issue without resorting to questions about the validity of the fossil remains that existed.

How are we to know, she'd ask, *that they're actually fossils? They could be lying to us, fudging the evidence*. It never felt like she believed what she was saying, as though she were picking some scripted responses the administration had typed and asked every teacher to study just in case their students had any questions. Our arguments, however, were short, quick, to the point, nothing my aunt felt the need to tell my mother (or, if she did, that my mother felt the need to address at home, glad that learning about the lives of dinosaurs helped motivate me in other areas: math, reading, science, any homework assignment I needed to complete before taking out my sketchbook and outlining another raptor, perfecting their dimensions, working on different variations, one with larger hind legs, one with its tongue sticking out, one with its claws tearing through a crosshatched lump of flesh and bone).

The drawings continued, but it wasn't till the fourth grade that I saw a shift in my talent and technique, that I could step back from a half-complete raptor and say, as objectively as I thought I was saying, that it looked like a velociraptor, even if it was the *Jurassic Park* rendition. My subjects' snouts became sharper, their eyes more keen, cunning, the claws appropriately sized, intimidating for the posture I placed them in, as well as for the prehistoric bushes and clouds lingering in the background, giving their bodies perspective. I learned how to angle my raptors so they appeared as though they were in mid-stride, one hind leg raised, the other pushing off the ground, ready to leap through the paper my palms were smudging less and less. I thought about making a flip book, showing one canvasing a forest for whatever dinosaur, regardless of size, its jaws could claim. Raptors didn't give a shit, they were raptors, and I was keeping their image alive in some small way, capturing their essence with a No.2 pencil, playing a kind of deistic god who, after bringing life to each of his new creations, no longer had nor wanted the authority to retouch anything, fearful that his eraser, worn and personified, would protest another smooth stroke across the paper, render the graphite into a thick smear.

I considered preserving their integrity, putting them in binder sleeves, or reserving a folder for each so I could file them away in some box, haul it around if we moved, store it in my closet, and pull it out whenever I wanted to showcase some of my more intimate things to a friend from school, or a new girl I was trying to impress. But I wasn't interested in starting a collection, in cataloguing drawings I would only look at two, maybe three times before casting them to my wall, taping them at the corners, pinning the sides until the batches of sketch paper would sometimes form the outline of a crooked cross I'd tell my mother was unintentional when she'd come in, examine me drawing on the floor, then look at the wall and ask why I just didn't put up the large wooden crucifix—the one with Jesus dying so dramatically, puncture wounds on his feet, knees, stomach, wrists—she had bought at the flea market in Mexico.

My latest drawings were always the ones I admired the most, and I remember the last meaningful one I drew with clarity: how I began with a line I wasn't sure about, feeling that it was too faint, that if I indeed wanted to turn it into a spine, it needed to be angled more diagonally, with more force the closer it sloped toward the base of the tail.

It was Saturday. My mother was still asleep in the next room. I had been up since six, watching cartoons, eating a bowlful of Apple Jacks and Pops. Since I saw no point in watching a barrage of new shows I didn't find as entertaining as *Power Rangers*, *Spider-Man*, and *Teenage Mutant Ninja Turtles* (series' that, a few years prior, I would have slept early on Friday nights to catch every episode of the following morning), I got my clipboard from the desk and a fresh sheet of printer paper from the packs my mother would bring home from work. I guided my pencil from the top left side of the paper down to the right, stopped, pondered if I should start over, and then placed the point on the tip of the line where I wanted the tail to be, stroking it downward to the left, curving it back up, and then back down to the left where the legs came into form. With my left hand, I slowly turned the paper and pivoted the pencil till I had an angle where I could envision the feet, and in particular the claw which would require more focus and maneuvering to get it into its sharp, famous shape. A few more turns of the paper, and already the hands had their fingers, the chest its neck, the head its jaws, minus the teeth. Without lifting the pencil, I had outlined the body, although it all seemed quite rudimentary, cartoonish, something from a coloring book or a paint-by-numbers kit, which in reality, was what I intended. If I could get the basic frame, the rest was just a matter of plugging in, the crosshatches, the squiggles, the range of shading to enhance its quality.

That afternoon, after sitting down as a family to eat my mother's spaghetti—a meal she'd make toward the end of the month when her bank account was descending toward a limbo of reds and negatives—I went back to my raptor, adding nuance to the tail, the claws, to the scaly region of its head. Slowly, with each short stroke of shade, I began realizing that this would be my best raptor yet. I knew that when I was done the next day, I would more than likely put my signature and the date on the bottom of the paper in a manner I always found very pretentious, yet professional, and that I would beg my mother to go to Wal-Mart so we could find a cheap frame, keep it from staining or from being ruined by the artificial light in my room which, because of its small size, would only intensify the south Texas heat that seeped so unsympathetically into our unairconditioned house.

I would usually draw the whole raptor first before shading in its features, but I felt inspired to challenge myself, to jump ahead, darken its complexion, flesh it out completely. I reached its arms before nightfall, and the next day, after accompanying my twin uncles to church—where I sat quietly between them and paid more attention to the manner in which the middle-aged priest tucked his static-colored hair behind his ears than to the sermon I was sure he had recycled from some earlier service, tweaking it here and there to fit his English-speaking audience—I plopped myself on the living room floor and picked up where I left off, completing the upper half of its body, the outstretched arms, the coal-colored claws, the alligator-scaled bottom of its neck, the top row of teeth (a few of which were missing, since I figured the repeated use and chomping on thick-skinned creatures would break one or two off, and would subsequently give it that authentic artist consideration and touch), the flaring slits of nostrils, the cat-thin pupils, the sharply inclined brows that somewhat anthropomorphized its features, but not enough to become a parody of itself, although the thought, and by extension the temptation, did cross my mind. I could ruin this, make it look ridiculous, a perfect body with a bobble head, and a smile lined with oversized human teeth, like some cartoon dinosaur on a children's show.

The thought faded. I kept drawing. Our house was silent. My sister was asleep in my mother's room. My mother was outside tending the clothesline, where our disembodied selves swayed with the spring wind that would sometimes seep through the window mesh, reluctant to fully toss itself in, as though our house were encircled with some sort of invisible spell the families that inhabited this plot of land before us placed on it, ensuring that whoever moved in would never experience the meaning of *cooling off*. I wiped the sweat beading down my forehead, jaw. I moved the paper farther out and smudged the last few parts that needed to be smudged. The raptor was done. My raptor was done. *That's it*, I said to myself, exhausted and sure that the numbness radiating from my forearm to my palms had developed into juvenile Carpal Tunnel syndrome. I stretched my wrist, snapped and popped it, jazz handed the pockets of stale air around me. I was scared to study what I had created, not because I feared finding any flaws, but because I felt, in true confidence-meets-cockiness fashion, that I had drawn something I wouldn't be able to outdo. And how could I when, no matter how many times I circled it, viewed it sideways, diagonally, upside down, I had no shame in admitting to myself that indeed it was great, that not only would my mother praise it the way she praised everything I did, but so would my uncles, my grandmother, my sister, my aunts, my cousins, friends at school who were interested in drawing, and who would undoubtedly be envious over the level of detail and realism I was able to achieve on paper, consoled only by my reiteration that there were always pterodactyls, stegosaurus, and an array of long-necked veggie eaters that still needed to be drawn.

I put my signature on the bottom right-hand side, an unconvincing cursive mixed with print *e*'s, each letter slanted and spelling the name *Steve*. Part of me believes my name deserves its own story, or at least a tangent within a story explaining its evolution: the *Stevie* I was called up to about second grade, uneventfully morphing into a *Steve* that lasted till middle school when an *n* suddenly appeared, and I responded to and introduced myself as *Steven* from that point forward, changing the spelling when I got older to *Stephen*, thinking that the *ph* gave it more sophistication, or that it would distract from my birth name *Esteban*, which was always lingering, hiding beneath my tongue, wary to be pronounced with a Spanish accent, thrown around as if I grew up speaking the language.

But digressions are for footnotes, poems even, something that doesn't require me to stray from the manner in which I heaved a small sigh of triumph as I unclipped the drawing, blew off the remaining eraser shavings, and put the paper on the printer we never used. I went to my room, occupied myself with an activity that was insignificant. Perhaps I took a nap, perhaps I put the piles of half-folded clothes scattered on the floor into the drawers, hanging the polos and pants in a closet that wasn't much more than a squared, sawed hole in the wall, uneven at the edges. An hour or two passed. I was hungry, and when I went into the kitchen to retrieve whatever leftovers hadn't succumbed to the refrigerated darkness spoiling their taste and consistency—foiled chicken, leftover spaghetti, slices of Little Cesar's pizza stuffed in Ziploc bags—I wandered into the living room, hoping that as I again observed the drawing, it would still give me the same feeling of artistic achievement when it came to rendering raptors in that which, as I believed at the time, was their most common and authentic form.

It wasn't there. I looked behind the printer, hugging it as though we were caught in the middle of a slow dance, moving to the rhythm of the rattling fan nearby that had been inching its way closer to the wall all morning. I squatted. My knees popped. I crawled beneath the cheap, poorly screwed stand whose legs were cobwebbed and glazed with the same white fuzz of dust that would manifest on the empty China cabinet, the TV set, the dining room chairs, the coffee table, the uncomfortable wooden panels on our couch's arms, accumulating overnight and appearing every morning when the sunlight, that slanted intruder, would filter in through the blind-raised windows and flush over our dusty furniture my mother would sometimes run her fingers across before work, already concocting a list of things to do when she returned home. There was no sheet of paper beside an unopened envelope of mail, or beneath the ball or two of crumpled napkins with orange-brown stains smudged from someone's fingers, cheeks, lips. I had lost remotes before, not realizing that they were still in my hand. I had lost my *Power Rangers* backpack at school, only to discover weeks after that a boy, someone I had never spoken to, had stolen it, scratched out the Sharpied name I had written on the inside of the main compartment, just along the zipper, and scribbled in his own, attempting to claim it was his even when my mother came to school and showed the administrator the receipt, said there was no reason for this little boy, only a grade below me, to scratch out his name and write it again. I had lost cartridges of N64 games—*Mario Cart, 007, Mortal Combat*—only to find them beneath the TV stand, or at the bottom of the plastic bin, where I thought I had already checked. I had lost my sister in the front yard once, unsure if she had gone around the house, where the neighborhood dogs would gather, linger, trot between our backyard and our grandmother's since there was no fence dividing our two lots, or if she had crawled beneath our home, squeezed her tiny body between the cinder blocks and entered that lopsided darkness acting as a limbo for missed baseball, Frisbees, objects that rolled in the slow, teasing pace they roll precisely when you don't want to lose them.

I scooted forward beneath the printer stand, sat cross-legged and craned my neck upward, trying to see if it got stuck between the stand and wall. Nothing. The back of my neck became hot, as though a handful of that endless Vicks my mother would rub on my chest every time I fell ill had just been lathered onto it. The warmth shot down my shoulders, flared along my spine before reaching the base of my ass, where it stayed for a moment, like day-after soreness, and then quickly spread to the front side of my body. I twitched, hit my head on the underside of the stand, and crawled out, feeling how I'd feel when I'd set up a blanket teepee between the stand and couches, plop in the middle with a bowlful of snacks, and turn the flashlight on and off, on and off, before leaving it off long enough to become convinced that there was someone hovering over my shoulder, waiting to join me.

I had no time to rub my head, to massage the small bump of its pain and swelling. I grabbed the printer and shook it, hoping that my drawing had somehow found its way into a crevice. Nothing flew out. I pushed it aside till it nearly landed on the couch and began running my hands against the stand and wall, as though they each contained a special kind of braille that would help me find the paper I couldn't see. I don't know where I learned what braille was, but I remember thinking that I was now blind, the drawing wasn't there because my eyes were no longer employed in their duty, and everything I thought I was seeing—the couch, the printer, the stand—was merely an afterimage, memories playing on repeat. The walls began to pulse, ripple as an onslaught of imaginary, horizontal raindrops began to pelt it, change its color, warp the already peeling, tobacco-brown paint. The room flipped a few times, spun slantwise like a globe, shifted out of focus and came back into a semblance of clarity when I heard my mother's voice say, "What are you doing? You okay?" She was wearing flip-flops, pink with clear straps, and her toenails—chipped of their bubblegum-pink polish—were still pretty, non-diabetic, evenly cut in what I could have mistaken for pedicure treatment, and undoubtedly more pleasant to look at than the stage they'd reach a decade later when they'd start to shrink and shrivel, sometimes fall off, flake, or cling to the cracked and callused skin that resembled dead tree bark.

"Mom," I said, "where—where is the drawing, the paper what was right—right here, right here?" I slapped the printer repeatedly, harder each time.

"What paper? There wasn't a paper there," she said, adjusting the basketful of folded clothes lodged between her flat hips and belly fat.

"The paper, Mom. The drawing!" I yelled, as I slammed the printer again.

"Wait, wait, wait," said my mother, walking around me and putting the basket on the couch, "you mean the one that was right here?"

"Yes, yes! Where is it? Where did you put it?"

"I thought it was trash. Like a sketch you didn't want anymore." My body grew warmer. There's a lighter behind my neck, I thought, like the kind my cousins—Ricky, Eloy, and Eddie, brothers that were always trying to up the pain factor with every prank—would steal from their father's jean pockets and use to burn each other's elbows, sneaking up behind them, or waiting till they fell asleep before pressing the flame against their skin. I was once their victim, but my role was usually that of accomplice, standing by them, being quiet, and perhaps because of my inability to forget even the simplest of things that made me feel guilty, this was karma, a strange sort of payback that was setting my body on fire.

"No. it wasn't trash, mom! It wasn't trash!"

"But why else would you put it on the printer? Why didn't you put it in your sketchbook? The one I bought you?"

"Be – because I – I didn't want to mess it up." My mother became blurry, her hair—brown, straight, manageable—was melting, sliding off her scalp, her arms stretched and thinned out, and her waist, snug beneath that red, sleeveless shirt she was wearing, began to shrink and sink back into itself. She looked like what I imagined people believe they see when they've claimed extraterrestrials paid them a visit in the middle of the night, a canvas of white light surrounding the creature's skinny, black figure as it throbs in and out of certainty, ambles closer toward a potential abductee with its large, swollen head and that rhythmic clicking of cosmic language. With the backside of my hand, I wiped the corners of my eyelids, but I couldn't shake my mother from her alien demeanor.

"Where is it? Where is it?" I cried.

"I thought it was trash. How was I supposed to know? You shouldn't put things there, Esteban," she said, searching the printer, pushing random buttons and sections as though it were a Japanese puzzle with a secret compartment that could reveal my drawing.

"You – you – you threw it away, didn't you?"

"Esteban, ay!" My mother moved the printer and stand, kneeled as far as her body allowed her to and began searching the lumpy linoleum.

"Did you put it in the trash?" I yelled, my chest squeezing under the weight of my stutter.

"You shouldn't've put it there. You shouldn't've. I bought you those sketchbooks for a reason."

"You threw it away, you threw it away!" I ran to the kitchen and began searching the trash bin, pulling the edges of the Hefty bag up, rummaging through the fast-food boxes and cups, the broken and still-greasy chicken bones, the soggy noodles my mother had scraped off our paper plates a few days prior, half-opened cans of beans with their lids nearly cutting my palms, as well as clumps of what appeared to be white rice, jalapeños, sliced tomato, small vegetables my sister and I discreetly forked to the side. I pushed my hands in deeper. Some pasta sauce-like substance spread across my forearms, nearly reaching my elbows.

"Don't do that, Esteban. It's not in there. Stop. Ya. Stop," she said, lifting herself slowly up. "I think I might've put it in the one outside." She rushed into the kitchen and pulled me away from the bin.

"You threw my velociraptor away! How come? How come?" I shimmied through her arms and bolted to the front door. It was heavy, but the sunlight seemed heavier, condescending even as I ran onto the porch, jumped off it and headed toward the green trash bin resting by our mailbox. Given my luck, I felt it wouldn't be in there. And if it was, it would've probably been torn, or smeared with moldy leftovers, muddled with the backwash of juice, soda, milk. Looking back, I see myself rounding the tree doing little to cast its shade across the parched blades of grass, and as I punched through the air, lengthened my stride, I could already see myself kicking and tossing the trash bin down, digging through it and ripping the plastic bags apart, until my mother comes and pulls me away, drags me back to the porch steps where she sits and I stand crying in her armpit, turning away, removing my hands slowly from my face, and watching as the bright spots and shadows reshape a world that seemed designed to never be on my side.

HEIST

I am seated near the middle of a long plastic table in a cramped room, the windows veiled with poorly cut green and yellow butcher paper. I am seemingly studious, halfheartedly taking notes, eyes locked on the woman scribbling chicken-scratch on the board as she says something that takes its time to arrive at my ears, muddled and slurred. She turns around, face twisting out of profile. She's my aunt Gloria. She points in my direction, and as she does— her chalk-coated finger straightened at an angle of authority—I act dumb, focus on the numbers listed behind her, pretend I have developed a sudden case of deafness.

"Which is the most important?" Her finger stabs the air again, her voice outdoes her first attempt at sounding like a Sunday School teacher, not an aunt. "Which is the most important?"

I cave. "Aren't they all?" She looks puzzled, unsure if I am serious or just full of shit.

"Well… technically, that's correct," she says, "but which one is the most important to you?" She contorts back into her lumbered posture, and I think of the eighth commandment, theft, *thou shalt not steal.*

My aunt furiously marks the board. Robin Hood immediately comes to mind—how folklore can make wrong actions both popular and right. Then I think of art heists glorified in movies, bank robberies, old gangsters, John Dillinger, Bonnie and Clyde, that inexplicable rush that renders my hands numb whenever I take one of my cousin's toys and place it behind the dresser, beneath the bed, denying that I knew where it was when they began accusing me of pulling the same old shit. Even when I'm not pulling pranks, objects have a way of seducing me. I don't return pencils. I bank change and crumpled dollar bills I witness spilling from my peers' pockets. I nab sweets from the refrigerator, conscientious of the fact that I'd already had more than my fair share.

And then there was that one Saturday at the grocery store with my mother. My aunt Rosa was looking after my sister, one less hassle my mother had to deal with as I ambled behind her, trying to keep pace with her catwalk-like stride, and knowing that if I was well behaved, she'd be more inclined to buy me a toy. We were in the frozen food section. My mother rested her elbows on the handle of the cart as she scanned the written items on her list. She scratched two or three things off, dividing her attention between the paper in her hand and the shelves of frozen corn, carrots, and broccoli, vegetables she'd microwave and mix in as a side for whatever we were eating, but which often just sat in the freezer for months on end, never once considered for the fresh scrapes and bruises my sister and I would happily sport when we'd come in, exhausted from play.

My mother yanked open a freezer door, took out a bag and tossed it toward the front of her half-filled cart. We rounded the corner, and I caught a glimpse of the toy section, small and less appealing than the ones I'd get so distracted by in Wal-Mart, Kmart even. I looked up at my mother. She met my gaze and just as I was about to look down she pointed at the toy aisle with her chin, saying, "You can go look at the toys, but just a little while. I'm gonna be around here so I'll come and get you when I'm ready." I nodded, but kept my eyes on her, unsure if what she had just said was true, that she was altering her grocery shopping routine—a routine that required my help if we were going to be in and out as quickly as possible, avoid any potential rushes at the checkout lanes—in order for me to entertain myself for a few minutes with a mediocre toy aisle.

"Go," she said, "and don't break anything."

"Okay," I said, and like a child trying to mask his excitement at a theme park—body tensing like the start of a spasm—I half-skipped, half-walked to the aisle, too overwhelmed to focus on anything particular. Then guns—not the Nerf, blaster, or water guns that lined the shelves at places like Toys "R" Us, but cheap rifles that merely made a firecracker-pop when you pulled the trigger, as well as nondescript handguns with the orange ring around the muzzle—came into view. I walked up to them, my right hand reaching over to touch the plastic stock, feeling like Adam, or perhaps God, in Michelangelo's fresco. It was cold, hard. It felt oddly comforting to know I was finding comfort in something I wasn't interested in, even if I knew how to use them, was by now, at eight, well versed in 12- and 20-gauge shotguns through the dozen-or-so hunting trips I took with my cousins and uncle. I ran my finger up to the trigger, then moved it back. I tried to imagine myself in the front yard, running from the porch to the tree to the fence, darting down the side of the driveway, where in my best black-ops stance, I'd fire rapidly at my sister, make my own sound effects when the clicking no longer kept up with my intention to pretend kill her, while she, like a good sport, would fake the amount of times she got hit, would fall back, stumble, run with her hands on her chest, yet never die.

I backed away, aware that this exchange of faux violence would undoubtedly venture into boredom once we had exhausted our invented characters and end-of-the-world scenarios. With my neck still craned, I walked down the aisle, scanned the action figures, the G.I. Joes, the caped crusaders and alien-faced villains from Saturday morning cartoon shows I didn't watch any more, the oddly shaped yo-yos, the medieval swords and shields, the large construction trucks and personified cars with eyes for windshields, smiles and teeth for grilles, each in their plastic boxes, neatly shelved and hanging, waiting to be purchased. I felt drawn to the toys that couldn't be used as weapons, could more easily imagine myself crashing the cars into each other, learning new tricks on the yo-yos, or adding voices to the action figures, making their hard, barely bendable bodies fly across my hands as I created storylines with no clear beginning, middle, or end, just action sequences that again sought to stop the already thousands of explosions defining my plotless world.

I grabbed a random action figure, slid if off the hook, examined the physique, the bulging constellation of muscles across a body that barely had any more room for muscles, the shoulder-length, brunette-fading-to-orange-colored hair, the black, blue, and red suit that molded so tightly to his skin, the utility belt, the boots, the emblem in the middle of his chest with some symbol that looked like the caduceus (although the word *caduceus* was still *medieval sword* in my eight-year-old vocabulary), and the description on the back of the package stating how this half-human, half-some-thing-or-another superhero was here to either save the planet or keep what had become of the earth from devouring us. I wanted it but wanted more to keep my options open in case my mother said no to this twelve-dollar toy. I slid it back on the hook and pushed it further back than where it originally was, thinking that if some other boy happened to wander into the aisle— searching for a toy, like me—he'd gloss over it, skip right into the girl section complete with pink and purple ponies, imitation Barbies, hairbrushes and tiaras, fake make-up sets, and small castles that evoke storybook memories of Rapunzel, Sleeping Beauty.

On the opposite shelves there were school supplies, notebooks, pencils, boxes of Sharpies, pens. I turned back around, aware I was getting toward the end, and as I scanned from top to bottom the last of these girl toys—the dolls, the teddy bears, the lockets—I looked down to find an upturned, half-opened package with the cardboard peeled back and the plastic squished, bent with the desperate impression of a child's fingers, fallen at my feet. There was a silver lightning bolt on the top right corner and immediately I knew the toy had something to do with the Power Rangers. Perhaps it was the Red Ranger action figure, or the Pink, the two most popular, or perhaps, given the size of the package, it was just some weapon from their arsenal, a wrist communicator, a Blade Blaster, a Power Sword, a Power Lance, a Power Axe, Bow, Daggers, or the Power Blaster that combined all of these weapons when the Rangers needed to destroy the growing monsters created by Lord Zedd and Rita Repulsa.

I looked behind me, looked in front. There was no one, not even a cart, odd for a Saturday afternoon, and I thought for a second that a sudden sale must have materialized in the front of the store, compelling everyone to stop what they were doing, forget what they came for, and head toward those half-off and two-for-one specials. Or was this something more serious, a large spill, an accident, a fight over the last discounted chicken, a disagreement over the number of coupons that could be used per customer? Was there a line-cutter, a crying baby I couldn't hear but that was annoying those unfortunate enough to be within listening-distance? Or maybe—since paranoia had a tendency to quickly creep its way into my imagination, cause a dramatic tangent in my line of thinking—this was that dreaded Rapture I had heard about from classmates who weren't Catholic, from Jehovah's witnesses that came by our house, standing on the porch like children on Halloween, waiting for a response to their claim that only those who had given their hearts and minds to God would survive the end of days, be accepted into heaven's light.

A streak of sunshine filtered in through the small, square windows lined just below the edge of the ceiling. I heard the sliding doors open. Footsteps shuffled across the large welcome mat. The wheels of some old, rain-rusted cart squeaked across the aisle next to mine and the general commotion of a grocery store returned to normal.

The intercom came on, grumbled like a distant lawnmower in need of oil, and a middle-aged woman's voice requested a manager's assistance on one of the express lanes. I looked behind me, looked in front. Still no one. I kneeled and began pretending I was tying my shoes. I unknotted the laces, tossing the inside lace toward the package. It wasn't long enough. I scooted up, tossed it again. I slid my left hand across and lifted the package. I saw Billy, the Blue Ranger, and with a slight cough and grunt, I flipped the toy over and went back to tying my shoes.

Carts in the surrounding aisles continued to squeak. Cash registers opened, items were scanned. I was alone. I studied Billy. He was a small figure with moveable limbs, half-sticking out of the molded plastic that held him. Besides him there was his Triceratops motorcycle, along with a sidecar attached to it, used to carry Kimberly. Both Billy and his motorcycle looked cheap, and it was precisely because of their cheapness—the badly painted patterns across his chest, the slightly distorted head, and the ability of this figure, like all the toys I owned, to withstand the constant thrashing and plotlines I would inflict upon it—that I saw them as beautiful, necessary to my happiness.

I looked up, looked ahead, looked behind. Again: no one. When I turned back around, however, I remembered there were cameras hanging from the rafters. They were spherical, black, attached with a long rod bolted to a beam. They were positioned in between two aisles, but you couldn't see the camera that was inside, whether it was facing north or south. They looked like the black droids at the beginning of *The Empire Strikes Back*, except hanging upside down, and if they were just as observant, I knew I wouldn't get away with what I was already planning. I stared hard at the camera, squinted, even waved with my hand—my trembling fingers grazing my jawline, like a child who had just learned to say goodbye. Then I lifted the package and with a good shake shook the Blue Ranger out and into my left palm. There was no eighth commandment to think about. No imaginary angel on my right shoulder reminding me of my religious duty. No secular thought or instinct that alluded to the morality I knew I should follow, had been following, and would continue to follow despite my lapses in judgment, my inability to foresee the way I'd feel once the action was complete. Despite my tendency towards an overactive conscience, all of these things evaporated in that moment. It was just me and Billy in his Blue Ranger suit, his motorcycle, and the memory of his adventures that played out on screen, his intelligence, his nerdy appearance, his quirky persona, his ability to invent gadgets all the Rangers used, his evolution into a quick, athletic, and competent leader, and his dependability, a quality I wanted to emulate, even if, by shaking him from his packaging, I was violating one of the principles that made him such a role model in the first place. Billy wouldn't approve, he would say something insightful, profound, convincing enough to deter me from my actions, and he would do so without the slightest hint of judgment, just a sincere attempt to understand the *why* of behavior.

But this Billy remained silent. I stuffed him in my pocket and began walking down the aisle back to where I started. My eyes darted toward the camera, then back down. I counted my steps in threes for some reason, *one, two, three, one, two, three.* My stride grew. My breathing muddled the noise around me. The rhythm of my heart increased to match the mood of this self-perceived, dramatic escape that any patron would have paid little attention to, not given a second look, not surrendered their train-of-thought to a boy with untied shoes who scurried with his head down until he found his mother in the frozen food section and immediately began helping her by choosing his and his sister's favorite hot pockets and pizza rolls, stacking the boxes carefully into the cart, while telling her—without staring up at that face that knew how to read his lies—that no, he didn't need a toy today, he'd rather the money go to necessities because he already had enough at home and didn't want to take advantage each time he was invited to the grocery store.

We traveled across the entire store before heading to the checkout lanes, where—while watching my mother put the groceries on the conveyor belt, whispering numbers as she came up with a total in her head—I stuck my hand inside my pocket and began fiddling with the Blue Ranger, testing the range of its limbs, wondering if its head could twist a full 360, and imaging how much damage it could take once I began contorting its body beyond its intended purpose, slamming it against the floor, tossing it on the couch, scraping its knees across the kitchen table because he had just escaped a fictional explosion on the stove, ready to save his friends being held captive somewhere in the living room. And just as I could see myself carrying him like a paper plane, mumbling more explosion noises and the *swoosh swoosh swoosh* of wind resistance slapping Billy's beat and blasted body, I could see my mother turning around from whatever she was cooking—light purple nightgown crookedly hanging from her shoulders, hair unraveled, as if she had just removed a set of pink rollers—and asking where I got that toy, that she doesn't remember it, that she's sure she'd remember it because the years may be wearing down her joints and skin but her memory was still thriving, and there was no way she could have bought that toy without her knowing, without a flashback coming to mind. *No way, no way.*

Shit, I thought. I released the Blue Ranger and took my hand out of my pocket. I could hide it, place it beneath my pillow each night, stuff it in the bottom of my bin, or just leave it in my backpack so my mother wouldn't find it. But what was the point of risking so much for so little? What was the benefit of not paying anything for something and having to limit myself in its use, and what use did I really have with this toy anyway, wouldn't I merely go on a binge when I got home and abandon it a few days later once I found a renewed interest in the alien spaceship from *Independence Day*, or the Caterpillar Power Loader from *Aliens*? Wouldn't I go back to the things I had already scratched, bent, and broken? Didn't I know I would first find fault with the extent of Billy's usefulness and then realize that perhaps the reason I was finding fault was, in fact, because I had acquired this toy unethically, taking it when I thought no one was looking, and violating the store's opportunity to profit from it, no matter how small the amount? Didn't I know myself?

"Get on the other side," said my mother, pointing to where the bagger was quickly stacking canned food into a bag already stretching under its new weight. I squeezed between my mother and the shelves of candy bars. The pocket where the Blue Ranger was nestled scraped the Milky Ways, Snickers, Hersey's, Reese's.

I was on the other side. The bagger looked at me. "Your shoes are untied, bud," he said.

"Oh," I uttered. "Thank you." I bent down and tied my laces sloppily, one loop larger than the other. I stood off to the side, suddenly noticing the number of cameras constellated throughout the store, one for every two aisles, two by the flower section, a few more by the pharmacy, and one by the entrance that seemed to have been installed after we had arrived, hanging lower than the rest, as if its job were specifically to catch children who had snuck items past their parents. Could the camera measure a change in temperature? Could it detect the nervousness of patrons who had something to hide? Could it see me, dazed by the consequences I would face should the detectors go off and that previously unintimidating security guard—heavy set, sweaty, and struggling to lift his baggy pants—were to stop his parking lot patrol and dart to the front of the store, eager to apprehend the criminal that set the employees and managers on high alert?

Once, several years earlier, as my mother and I were leaving Wal-Mart, bags of items sagging in our hands, two teenage boys sprinted past us and broke through the crowd of people coming in and out of the entrance, while a security guard and a female manager scurried after them. There wasn't much context needed to understand what was happening: the boys had stolen something, something small enough to fit in the pockets of their black jeans, or beneath their oversized black and white tees (ironically, I remember bearing what appeared to be an airbrushed painting of the Virgin of Guadalupe displayed across the back, the kind artists painted in front of you at fairs). In those days, our town Wal-Mart was flanked by a large grassy lot that sloped downward before leveling off for fifty or sixty yards, where it was met by a chain-link fence and uncut, shoulder-high bushes and brush that gave the viewer the feeling that what lay beyond was something swampy, murky and wet. And that's exactly where those two boys (or was it fugitives at this point?) were running toward, a long expanse of soggy uncertainty, an existence where their photos would be posted on the nightly news and a toll-free number would be listed just below their blurry faces.

My mother and I found ourselves walking faster, nearly skipping across the sidewalk just to catch a better view of the chase. The Virgin of Guadalupe boy was shorter, larger, slower, and even as he separated from this accomplice, bolted toward the rows of houses where we lived, the security guard was able to tackle him to the ground and, with what looked like a pair of toy handcuffs purchased from that exact same Wal-Mart, secure his wrists, lift him up, and slowly begin escorting him back towards the parking lot. They appeared serious at first, exhausted, coming off the adrenaline, but the closer they came, the more I thought I saw them talking, smiling, laughing lightly, the way strangers do when they strike up a conversation, as though this were merely a game, a test to measure the response time from Loss Prevention. The female manager met him halfway and both she and the security guard turned around for a moment to watch the other boy jump the fence, fade into my imagined murkiness.

"Stop him! Stop him!" shouted a voice behind us. I turned around and another manager, goateed and large, was pointing at a bald teenager who, without looking back, immediately raised his hands.

"I didn't take nothing. Search me, I didn't take nothing." He had a smirk across his face, one that to my eyes suggested to me that he didn't care how rough they handled him, how many questions they asked, how long he was kept in custody, because despite everything they would claim they had on him, he believed, in that moment, that he was going to walk away. And even if he did go as far as saying that yes, he did indeed know the other two boys—they were friends, acquaintances—he'd argue that they acted on their own free will, that he had no prior knowledge of their intentions and would have dissuaded them had they hadn't committed their act so fast. The security guard restrained him, told the crowd to back away, and yanked both of the boy's hands behind his back.

"Stevie, let's go," said my mother, already heading toward the parking lot. The manager mumbled something into his walk-ie-talkie and the security guard shoved him back into the store. There were police sirens wailing. The cars in the lot slowed down, both passenger and driver trying to see past the commotion. "Let's go," said my mother again, and her voice faded with the whispers and mumbles sprouting around us.

"Stevie. Stevie." My mother's voice snapped me back to the checkout line, to the Ranger in my pocket. "Come on, we gotta pick up your sister. I told Rosa I'd only be an hour and I hate . . . ." She pushed the cart past me, still talking. I ran to her, clung to her side and pretended to listen. She looked motherly, worried about picking up my sister and getting back home before the frozen food and ice cream thawed and melted. I grabbed the cart handle. My mother moved her hand to the middle. She was now my accom-plice, or at least that's how it would play out on camera. The de-tectors didn't sound. We were out. The security guard nodded at my mother. She didn't nod back, kept talking. ". . . and you're just gonna stay in the van with the windows down. Rosa's gonna talk forever if we both get off. Wait," she stopped, placed her left arm out in front of my chest, and asked as though I'd know the answer, "did they put the chicken in?"

"The chicken?" I uttered.

"Yes, ay, don't tell me they didn't put it in." She began rum-maging through the bags. Boxes of noodles spilled out, jars of spa-ghetti, pickles, and jam banged against each other. "Son of a . . . They didn't put it in. Put those back, please," she said, pointing at the small disasters she had created. "I'm gonna go back in and get it, just stay here. Actually, go to the palm tree over there, look." I turned around and studied the palm tree: short, depressed, in desperate need of a beach backdrop that would make its slumped posture more important, scenic. When I turned back, my mother was already inside, intent on getting our missing chicken.

I pushed the cart down the sidewalk, toward the palm tree. The security guard eyed me, then went back to scanning the customers, his hand on his belt buckle, like an amateur actor trying too hard to land the part of the sheriff in a Western. The sun grew warm on my face, scratching my cheeks. There was mulch spilling from the concrete ledge squared around the palm tree, looking like a toppled vase full of potpourri. I kicked a piece across the sidewalk. I picked one up, tossed it at the leaves. It shook with the same suddenness front yard branches shake before a storm, and just as I was about to consider the meaning of this comparison, interpret it in a manner to fit my mood, I remembered the way I felt in the aisle and took the Blue Ranger from my pocket, bent down, and began burying it in the mulch. My shoelaces needed to be tied again, I told myself. I could trip. I could fall in the parking lot, scrape my hands, my skull, break my head open and burden my mother with a hospital bill she couldn't afford. I hit dirt and dug my fingernails deeper, expecting to hit concrete anytime soon. It didn't come. I stuffed Billy in, spread the dirt over, piled on more mulch than necessary, and then examined my little burial.

"Stevie."

I've been caught, I thought. She's seen my crime, witnessed it and said nothing, as though she were hoping, and more important-ly expecting me to stop what I was doing, confess, and take responsibility for my sins. I grabbed my shoelaces, twisted them quickly, looked up and saw my mother silhouetted against the partial halo of the sun. "Are you ready? Let's go. Your sister, don't forget." I tugged the laces harder and ran to the cart. My mother, time saver extraordinaire, pushed the cart over the ledge and nearly sprinted toward our van, nestled between other sunburned and oil-starved cars. As I gripped the inside of her elbow, I felt someone staring at me, willing to wait as long as it took for me to return.

DUEL

Beside the condemned remnants of my stepfather's mother's small, box-shaped shack of a house, there's an empty lot that still acts as a shortcut for the residents of the housing projects on the other side who, for decades, have ambled through with a stride slow and staggered enough to suggest their lives are the most burdened in the world, leaving behind uneven trails that make this parched, trash-riddled space of land seem like it was mowed by teenagers who had never learned an efficient pattern for their summer job.

Before my mother, my sister, and I moved into a neighborhood with clean lawns, garages, residents who took their dogs for a walk, or who sat outside in lawn chairs talking, waving, smiling at passersby without any apparent hint of suspicion, we lived next to my grandparents, who lived in front of my stepfather's mother and her sun-singed dwelling that, from a distance, did indeed look quaint, authentically Southern, made for storybook dwarfs and elves, until you came closer, saw the termite-pocked wood, the crumbling cinder blocks, the splintered porch steps, the overgrown flowers I never knew the names for, the steep, wooden ramp my stepfather built for his mother and her wheelchair, one of the few times in his life, according to my mother, where he put someone else's needs ahead of his own.

There were things about that house that evoked feelings I couldn't quite explain, how the shy yet intricate webs of shade cast by the two trees—one in middle of the yard, the other by the side, leaning its thin, twisted trunk against the waist-high chain-link fence—moved across the lawn like the shadow of a dress on church marble, or like it was mourning something other than the obvious fact that my step-grandmother was dying, had the skin of a dead rose petal, had the spine curved like a dead rose, too, and whose voice now sounded like that of a smoker who can only speak through an electrolarynx, muttering spurts of syllables in Spanish I couldn't understand the one or two times I met her, shook her hand, smiled as though I was excited to be in her shriveled presence, thinking that my own grandmother wasn't that far off, that her crow's feet already resembled discounted pottery, that her fingers were arthritic, unable to lend their loyalty to the idea of lifting anything that wasn't dishware or the variety of plants she'd buy at flea markets and roadside stands, and that her overall view on life was prolonging the last five to ten years of her declining health, the worsening diabetes, the slowness that limited her gardening and the household duties she felt more keen not only on completing but perfecting after my grandfather passed into that complex, Catholic notion of an afterlife, intent on preserving a house one of her nine children could proudly inherit.

When my stepfather died—killed in a late-night drug deal that strayed from the quick and nonviolent course his drug deals usually took—his mother was moved into a nursing home, and the house was taken over by one of the daughters, who once or twice a week would stop by, pull weeds from the yard, take boxes of things out, inspect the bottom of the roof for bee or wasp hives, or for the general deterioration that had begun to afflict the wood long before I was born, then lock the gate and leave, returning weeks later to repeat the process, until one day the curtains were removed, announcing to whomever had been giving their attention to this slow withdrawal that the visits would no longer continue.

The place had a history I couldn't fully appreciate whenever I'd find myself studying the heavy-handed loneliness before catching my breath and returning to whatever game had me running across my grandmother's front yard during family barbecues, or when I was crossing the street with some of my cousins to reach the empty lot beside it, unable to see the significance I can now say it was hoping to be seen with, as though the memory every abandoned house contains can personify its own structure enough to make it seem to the more sympathetic observer that it wants to be remembered.

I recall staring at it briefly one particular afternoon, as I ran to the center of the empty lot and began swiping my foot across my moundless pitcher's mound. I spiked my heel, twisted it and looked up to find my cousin Ricky a few yards off, knees bent, hands in front of his chest, like a runner waiting for a baton to be passed, ready to kick the red kickball I was rolling in my hands in a manner I thought of as professional, unafraid, serious, intimidating enough to psych him out of any notion that his shoe would make contact on his first swing. Though football was the sport we'd usually play when we got together, enthused about trying out the short passes and Hail Marys we saw the Cowboys make the previous Sunday, it was summer, and there were only four of us—me, Ricky, Eloy, and Eddie—enough, sure, to make two teams of two, but not as fun as when our other seven or eight cousins were present, and when our twin uncles, in their twenties and still living with my grandmother, would join in, be the quarterbacks for each team, lead us in keeping with our idolatry of them, of their street cred, carrying our teams into another small victory.

Eddie was kneeling behind Ricky, tying the laces of his white and black imitation Nikes which, like mine, had accumulated so much dirt from constant use—school, recess, little league practice—that there was little difference now between the knockoffs and the real ones, and no self-consciousness or embarrassment that followed whenever there were other kids around, looking me up and down, noticing my shoes and, if they were friends, asking where I got them. *A gift from one of my aunts,* I'd always say, *a gift from one of my aunts.*

"Let's go Ricky!" shouted Eddie, as he stood up, wiped his hands, popped his fingers and jumped up and down, loosening his limbs. He was the youngest and least athletic of his brothers—Ricky and Eloy—and since he and I were the same age, only a month apart, we naturally had to compete against each other, especially when his mother, my aunt Rosa, would begin discussing her boys at family events or gatherings, divulging their habits, their personalities, what they did and didn't like, how quick they were each growing, and how she was sure that Eddie was already taller than me, there was no doubt, *Mira, look*, she'd say as she'd snatch us by our shirt collars from whatever we were doing, spin us around so our backs were pressed against each other, and with her hands hovering over our heads, as if she were about to do a magic trick, begin comparing our heights, claiming that even though Eddie was a month younger, he was taller by at least an inch. It was all size and numbers with her, except when it came to school grades, a subject she'd either avoid or respond to by telling my mother that academics shouldn't always define boys our age. We were young, and what happened outside of the classroom was often times more important than what happened in it. Eddie would indeed surpass my height (eventually eclipsing his older brother Ricky to become the tallest in the family), a sudden growth spurt that hit him his sophomore year in high school rendering his once thin and short demeanor into a rugged, robust, and raw figure ready to take on any game-time situation, though he only played half a season of JV football, trading what any high school coach would have said was at least second-string tight-end material for an after school job at a Chinese buffet.

Despite what he would or would not become, that afternoon, he was the weakest team member, his height no compensation for the fact that he was the slowest runner, the most uncoordinated, unable to match even me when it came to speed or agility. He had only enthusiasm going for him, and I knew that even if Ricky did kick the ball to center field where Eloy was standing, watching intently, confident that his favorite cousin could challenge his older brother, Eddie would be up next, and there was no doubt that I could strike him out, or curve the ball in such a way that he would clip it awkwardly in my direction—make it easy to hurl it at his body—or that he would hit it high enough for me to catch it, giving me the opportunity I was already envisioning in my head to look him in the eye, call *Out* softly, and walk back to the mound, triumphant.

"You got this, Ricky," said Eddie, "Stevie ain't got nothing on you."

"Let's go batter, batter, batter, batter, batter, batter, batter!" yelled Eloy behind me. I looked around briefly and saw him smiling, hunched over, swinging his body side to side, punching his right hand into his left palm, eager to spew the latest baseball lingo and shit-talk he had learned. I turned around, raised the red ball up to my chest—my nose and mouth covered by the worn rubber—and quickly, thinking too much about form, tossed it down the middle, where Ricky, who had perhaps been watching this all in slow motion, waited till the ball made contact with the tip of his shoe and soared past me. I wanted to dive for it, but there were constellations of tiny ant hills immersed within even larger ant hills all across the lot. Plus, the grass was parched, and having fallen on this same ground more than one occasion—Thanksgiving, New Year's Eve, Christmas, holidays that lent themselves to impromptu games of football—my skin was well acquainted with the dirt and dead grass' sandpaper texture. The catch wasn't worth my body's sacrifice. Still, I leaned to my side and stretched my left arm out. I stumbled a bit, turned around and saw Eloy anticipate the ball's trajectory, opening his arms as if he were welcoming a dog that had not seen its owner all day. Ricky ran. His long ponytail cinched with three rubber bands at the end, the middle, and near his scalp was swinging, scraping his neck as he rounded first base and stopped midway to second, going back after Eloy cocked the ball over his head, dared him with a smile to run a little further. Each of our bases were nothing more than pieces of torn Styrofoam cups we had found by the curb or my step-grandmother's chain-link fence, and because the last of the springtime wind was on vacation—occupying some beach, I imagined, in the Caribbean, adding character to the palm trees, serenity to the sails off on the ocean's distance—our bases stayed in place, sunk beneath the overused pressure of our soles.

Eddie shouted something enthusiastic, younger brotherish, and began clapping, unembarrassed by this public display of what Eloy and I would later claim was *sucking up* to an extent that we had not only never seen before, but that we knew—the moment he shouted in that squeaky tone—was his attempt to compensate for his lack of talent on the field.

"No worries, Stevie," said Eloy, walking closer, still holding the ball above his head, "you got the next one."

I nodded, let out a deep breath, and caught the ball with my chest. We had agreed beforehand that we weren't allowed to steal bases, but from my peripherals I saw Ricky take his foot off first, squat and hawk a loogie in my direction, and say in that hoarse, post-puberty voice, "He's a sucky pitcher, Eddie. It's all straight, he can't curve it." He was right, I couldn't curve it. But I had my own strategy: rolling it as close to his legs as possible, tripping him up and watching as he angled his body awkwardly, unsure where he should put his right foot, much less his left one.

I composed myself, brought the ball up to my face again, and hurled it across the ground. Eddie, somehow sensing my intentions, stepped back to anticipate the pitch, but he was too late, and all I could do was chuckle at the manner in which he pivoted on his left foot and swung with his right, clipping the ball so that it rolled back on his shin, bounced off his knee, and shot into the air where he stared at it the way a child stares at fireworks, apparently thinking that if he leaned his torso back far enough, he could still kick it. He extended his leg halfway up, and the ball rolled off his chest and upward over his left shoulder. Eddie stumbled back.

"Ha, ha!" yelled Eloy from across the field, like Nelson from *The Simpsons.*

"That was a slow one, Eddie. Come on, you got this," encouraged Ricky, walking back to his base. The ball took a few bounces before stopping short of rolling onto the street. Eddie picked it up, wiped away the dirt and tiny balls of stickers our skin and shoes would often be subjected to, then headed back to the undefined borders of the plate. He tossed the ball back to me and shrugged his shoulders, relaxing the visible stiffness that had been interfering with his form, causing him to stand awkwardly, unsure where to place his hands, how he should look, what pattern his breathing should take other than the forced silence complementing the forced stoicism that did little to show how unfazed he was by my initial toss.

I tossed the ball in the same manner again, and when again he couldn't make contact, shuffling backward like those clowns I once saw at a frontage road circus juggling bowling pins, daggers, hula-hoops, a combination of objects that upped the ante on their performance, he shouted "Stop it, Stevie!" and gave me an annoyed-going-on-angry look that did nothing to compensate for the fact that commands never come off as intimidating when they include the name *Stevie*.

"Don't do that again. Pitch it right, güey!" he yelled, his voice sounding like mine when I knew I had to confess to my mother that I did something wrong, each stuttered word crumbling under the weight of anticipated tears.

It was one of the rare times I heard him use the word *güey*, a Mexican Spanish term for *dude*, developed and taken from the word *büey* (*ox*) somewhere in Mexico, and smuggled into the English language the way Spanish slang seemed to be smuggled into the vocabulary of Valley boys like my cousins who, although they couldn't speak Spanish fluently, were well versed in the harsher words that so easily molded to their tongues. I'd hear the word *güey* more prevalently in high school, in the hallways where it was used either in a friendly tone amongst those students who spoke Spanish at home and couldn't escape the language barrier that kept them in regular courses, or by those students who administratively belonged to the same category, but outside of school gave their loyalty to different factions, gangs, and who upon stumbling into each other between classes—whether intentional or not—as I witnessed on a few occasions, would begin shouting, *Whatcha looking at, güey? What, güey? You wanna go or what? I don't give a fuck where you're from, güey, I'll still fuck you up!*, followed by a few shoves that turned into poorly-executed upper cuts and jabs, an all-out brawl that would make me take a few steps back before angling myself against the sudden crowd, jostling not for the best but for the safest position, the view that would allow me to talk about the incident during lunch, restate how it all started—their encounter, their dialogue, their repeated use of the word *güey*—without actually getting involved myself. Though my high school friends and I would parody the word, imitate the semi-intimidating manner in which it was spoken, even use it in basketball when a play didn't go our way and all my teammates and I could do was laugh at our inability to properly execute, I thought of it as a term used only when matters turned serious, remembering that afternoon, as I often did, when my twin uncles, then just teenagers themselves, had confronted my stepfather, Santos, urging him to stay away from my mother, shouting *She doesn't want to see you, güey. Stop fucking bothering her!*, and on and on they went, until their voices could no longer sustain two languages that were doing nothing to keep him from understanding that my mother had no intention of reconciling, much less allowing him to visit his daughter.

"I'm just throwing it," I said.

"But throw it straight. You're throwing it right at my feet."

"That's the way kickball works," I said, unsure if I should let out the cackle bubbling in the back of my throat.

"Stop it, Stevie. You know what I mean. Just throw it down the middle."

"It curves, Eddie. That's what friction does to it. The ball loses speed and then it curves," I said, evoking a scientific concept I wasn't all too familiar with, but that I hoped would shut Eddie up, make him understand that there was a good chance the ball was going to follow that trajectory again, and he shouldn't at all be surprised when it did.

"Just down the middle," he said.

"Okay," I responded, gathering myself into my stance.

The ball went down the middle, not because I decided to appease him at the last second, but because I was trying too hard *not* to and in the quick knee-to-chest motion that came before the pitch, I overthought the ball's trajectory and let it slip from my fingertips too soon, sending it precisely along Eddie's requested path. His foot connected with the ball this time, and he hit it just over my head. I had no time to react, to jump, extend my arms, make a significant attempt at stopping the ball. Ricky was already rounding second by the time Eloy caught it on its second bounce and thinking that instead of running toward him like I did, I would be running toward home, he hurled it across the field in my presumed direction. The ball bounced into the street. Ricky rounded third and scored, chuckling as I hurried past him then stopped, looked both directions, knowing that the amount of traffic that street saw was limited to residents, people who were lost, and police cruisers making their weekly rounds, yet unable to break my habit of caution.

I retrieved the ball from my grandmother's yard, that strip of grass between the curb and fence, and tossed it back to Eloy, who had come up from center to cut Eddie off. Though he was out of breath, Eddie still managed to contort his face into a smirk, and the expression, slowly growing, cutting across his cheeks, widening like the Joker's (the Jack Nicolson version), stung me. It wasn't supposed to. I was supposed to have triumphed. I shouldn't have found myself seeking one of the few biblical references I knew, found myself feeling like Abel, that Eddie had somehow betrayed me by kicking the ball and killed a part of my bodily self by making it to third (which, at least numerically, heightened the religious allusions I was learning to thoroughly construct and interpret in my head). He wasn't my brother. We were far from close, and yet there was a sense that if we had indeed shared something special—playing kickball, sleeping over at each other's houses during the weekend, or breaking the rules and shouting during our orderly transitions between class periods, *Hey, that's my cousin*—his surprising physical feat during this moment and my subsequent embarrassment had made him my rival, eliminated our previous camaraderie, made it impossible not feel as though the entirety of our relationship would, from here on out, be divided into permanent eras of before and *after*.

The last time I saw Eddie, some fourteen years after this particular game of kickball, he was seated with his wife and family at the front table of a dance hall for Ricky's daughter's quinceañera, a celebration and passage into womanhood I had always found premature, boring, structured off the same routine of countless other quinceañeras that included young, professional, and tuxedoed dancers from Mexico, a slideshow, a father-daughter dance with a song that was purposefully too sentimental, an announcer providing a play-by-play of the games and whatever choreographed performance was up next, and the half-lit sea of immediate and extended family members that were either over- or underdressed, never in the middle. I arrived late, silhouetting the view of the front tables during one of the performances where the male dancers led the *damas* (dames) in a dance that appeared to have been half-perfected only a few weeks prior. My fiancée made a mad dash to the table where my mother and sister were sitting, and I—shoulders hunched, hands slightly up, like some timid contestant being introduced on a game show—trailed her too slowly and midway through began waving and mouthing *Hi* to Eloy, Eddie, Rosa, and her husband Enrique, a short, unshaven man who had aged only in his teeth—the years of smoking and Bud Light having rotted the enamel to the point that every word seeping through his breath sounded like bullshit—and who always looked unenthused, at least whenever I saw him, about the place and situation he was in, having preferred—as was so often rumored amongst my mother and my other aunts, as well as by his slumped over posture, his blank expression, the sleep-deprived eyelids that sunk further in upon themselves—a life lived on the road, traveling from city to city in his semi, dropping off supplies and goods for a company I'm not even sure my aunt Rosa knew the name of, just driving, driving till the memory of things like this quinceañera was safely a few states away.

Eloy, Rosa, and Enrique smiled, but Eddie, arm wrapped around his wife as though she were about to leave him, didn't. He merely watched as I crossed his path and then averted his eyes back to the dance. My mother gave her usual introduction, a hug, a kiss on the cheek, and proceeded to demand with her eyes and slight head tilt that I personally greet everyone, a task I've always hated the way one hates a particular food item, that unbearable task of subjecting yourself to something that could have easily been avoided.

"I'll wait till the dance is over," I said, pointing at the performance. My mother put her elbows on the table, and began asking my fiancée how we were, what was new in our lives, how were things with the wedding coming along, and so on. I squeezed myself between my sister and her boyfriend, and, caught in that same awkward, sorry-I-came-so-late stance, I smiled and said hi again to Rosa, Eloy, and Eddie, and while Rosa and Eloy, straining their attention though the glittery darkness, managed to smile in return, to raise their eyebrows and tilt their heads back to acknowledge my presence, Eddie once again did not return the gesture. We had not seen each other in years, not since a chance encounter at the gas station where he had whistled to me and shouted "Hey!", and I, not expecting to meet anyone on a rainy, Friday evening, went over, all smiles, half-hugging him and commenting that I was amazed at his height, asking where he was going.

"Chicago," I thought I'd heard him say, "Me and my dad are going to Chicago, but we're stopping in Houston and Dallas and a few other places in between, but we've got a lot of business in Chicago."

Now he was ignoring my greetings, impassive and seemingly intent on ensuring that his mime-like demeanor went noticed not only by me, but everyone around him. I sat down, looked over, unsure why I wanted his attention, why I felt like I needed it. I was the one, given what good fortune I could claim, who should've been shunning him, but the scene had derailed from my expectations and I had no idea how to gain the upper hand. Ten, fifteen, thirty minutes passed. I made my rounds with my family, feigning interest in my cousins' children, saying things were good when asked, being briefly interrogated by aunts and uncles who, given the manner in which they lazily asked their questions, how their eyes moved between me and the blur of silhouettes pulsing around us, seemed as if they, too, wanted to skip the small-talk, but were bound by politeness to inquire about my life.

Somewhere between discussing what type of spirits we liked and didn't and noting the venue's chandeliers, I looked over at Eddie, still wondering why he would have ignored me so publicly, what his reasons and motivations were. He was drinking Budweiser, still holding his wife, staring at another uneventful performance that unfurled across the dance floor. And then, as though he had never really noticed me until this moment, he suddenly smiled briefly and waved me over with his right index finger the way a mobster would one of his henchmen. Knowing this, that I was being summoned by a cousin I had every advantage over—stable job, salary, college education, a fiancée, and plans to move to Austin in the next year because the Valley had grown too small for us, too familiar, we were ready for bigger things, culture, food, museums—I went over eagerly. I moved around my fiancée, lowered my stance, and leaned closer to Eddie, listening closely, expecting the music blaring in the background to drown out whatever he was about to say and wanting to make sure I could hear.

"Are those glasses for show or what?" he asked.

Glasses, I thought? What the hell does he mean by glasses? We were using plastic cups for the alcohol, not glasses, and just as I was about to turn around, second-guess myself and wonder if my fiancée and I, as well as the rest of the people at the table, had indeed decided that if we were going to celebrate, clear plastic cups didn't represent or reflect our mood, I realized he meant my tortoiseshell glasses, the ones my mother bought me when I came back from college, employed as a barista and still on her insurance, the ones that I'd receive compliments on by teenage girls and women in their early twenties who said they were *Cool, Awesome, Pretty sweet.* I chose them at the suggestion of an ex-girlfriend, and they were now at the center of my conversation with a cousin who had, from my perspective, grown considerably envious and bitter toward everyone.

"I've had these glasses for years. I have to legally wear them," I said, chuckling to veil my confusion while adjusting the rims. "It says it on the back of my driver's license."

"They look like they're just for show," he said, shaking his head. His wife turned around, looked up, smiled at me, then went back to her conversation with Eloy's wife.

"Nah, they're kind of old now. I gotta get new ones soon," I said, remembering that I had been wearing these same glasses at the gas station convenience store the last time we'd run across one another, and that he had said nothing then, perhaps at the time too distracted by my long hair and neck beard to have noticed or cared.

Eddie lifted his left arm from his behind his wife's shoulder and reached over for his beer. His prolonged sip told me he was done with the conversation.

"It was nice to see you, man." I patted his shoulder.

"You, too," he nodded into his beer.

I walked away, confused.

Back on the mound, I watched Eddie awkwardly hock a loogie, wiping away the string of phlegm swinging from his lips.

I pitched to Ricky next, got him to kick into my hands. He switched with Eddie at third, and on Eddie's at bat, he sailed the ball to center. Eloy grabbed it on one bounce and got Eddie out when he got too cocky and rounded first for second, hitting him just below the waist. Ricky scored, came up to the plate again, and hit the ball past me on his next attempt, jogging safely to first.

"I'm gonna bring you home," Eddie said to Ricky, calm, confident, credible. I knew he was going to hit it: this was kickball, and the chances of striking anyone out were limited to toddlers and adults who'd failed P.E. class as teenagers. My own confidence faltered. Quickly, I devised a new plan.

I tossed the ball slowly, wanting him to kick it because statistically, I thought, it would be easier to end the inning with Ricky on first. Eddie swung, but clipped the ball with the side of his shoes, almost falling in the process. Relieved, my confidence restored, I laughed, watched as Eddie retrieved the ball, and then laughed again when he tripped on the laces he had a bad habit of tying poorly.

"You ain't gonna be laughing when I kick this straight into your face."

"All your kicks have been lucky," I said.

"It isn't luck. You're just a sucky pitcher."

"You're a sucky everything," I said, flinging the insult back at him, newly emboldened. "The only reason you ever win is because you join Ricky's team. You're not good at shit and you know it." The words escaped my lips before I really considered them, faster and meaner than usual.

"Stevie, Stevie," I heard behind me, and I couldn't tell whether it was Eloy or Ricky, their voices muddled by my adrenaline, by the beads of sweat from my scalp rolling onto my forehead and temples, by the sound of my heartbeat racing into my eardrums, pulsing into a *dum-dum, dum-dum, dum-dum,* before Eddie's voice pierced the rhythm and, with his arms outstretched and his mouth jumping ahead of his voice, like a badly-dubbed kung fu movie, I heard him shout:

"What the fuck. Take it back, Stevie."

A sudden wave of nausea moved through me, shuddered the lot and surrounding houses out of focus. The ball became heavy in my hands, like my uncles' sets of dumbbells they'd sometimes ask me to try out just so they could watch me squat and clumsily use my thighs, hips, and stomach to lift the twenty-five-pound weight to my chest. As I shook the fuzziness clogging the corners of my eyelids, Eddie began to take shape before me once again, until at last I could make out the anger in his face, note that his body was squared up with mine. His nose mere inches from my brow.

"Why?" I said, leaning in despite my growing fear, my anger taking over. "It's true, you always nag and cry when Ricky doesn't pick you. I bet he doesn't even want to pick you."

"Stevie, just pitch the ball," said a voice I still couldn't distinguish, approaching at a hurried pace.

"That's why Eloy picks you, 'cause we all feel sorry for you. That's why Roy and Chris pick you last when we play football," said Eddie, alluding to our other cousins, who contrary to his comment, always chose me second or third, but never last, last was reserved for our even younger cousins Johnny and Daniel, who we had to choose because of our aunt Inez's insistence and complaints to our mothers that their sons had never learned the idea of inclusivity.

"You don't even know what you're talking about," I shouted, my feet shuffling forward, my hands releasing the ball from the tight squeeze I had inflicted upon it, the tension—without the ball as an outlet—now flooding my forearms, elbows.

"What, you can dish it out but you can't take it?" asked Eddie, walking closer, wiping his hands on his shirttail.

"I'm not the one who's getting all butt hurt because he can't hit the ball right."

"Stevie! Eddie! Just play!" shouted the voices behind me, too slow to keep pace with how quickly I began moving, jogging toward Eddie, saying things I would have had to pay for with my mother's quick and consistently moral tongue if I had ever said them in front of her or in the presence of my grandmother or one of my aunts.

"Take it back!" shouted Eddie again, advancing, no more than a few feet away now, making his hands into fists and lifting them to his head like an amateur boxer in a sparring match.

"No! You suck!" I shouted. I sped toward him, and as he mirrored my actions, darted with my signature Robocop arms—a move he learned from me after I told him that it made people run faster—I lunged forward and pushed him in the chest, and he stumbled backwards, his body turning 180 degrees, dropping slowly until he broke his fall with his hands and jaw. The dirt plumed around his legs. The sun shone through the small columns that rose and dissolved into the air like firework smoke. He turned around quickly, only to find me jumping on him, straddling his waist. He struggled with my hands as I gripped his collar, suddenly—uncharacteristically, urgently—hell-bent on slamming his neck and head over and over into the dirt until he understood what a shitty player he was.

"Stevie! Eddie!" shouted Ricky and Eloy, their cries growing in volume.

Eddie growled between his hiccup-like grunts and bared teeth, "What do you want to do, sex me? You want to sex me or what?"

Though I was familiar with the *shits*, the *fucks*, the *goddamnits* I'd pass around in class like love notes—hoping they'd surpass the realm of cheesiness and become meaningful—more direct language was at times too much for me to grasp, and the word *sex*—unlike the word *fuck*, which connoted physical intimidation or altercation, to my mind—was too literal, too heavy-handed, would immediately cause me to blush when I'd catch adults speaking about it in public, in the nooks of restaurant booths, in the aisles of bookstores, in the frozen section at the supermarket where I once heard, and through my peripherals saw, a man—slightly overweight and no older than a college student—say that a woman's breasts, or *tits* as he said it, were no larger than two pints of ice cream he had placed on his chest, cookies and cream I think was the flavor. Unlike *fuck,* the word *sex* implied intimacy, or that strange amount of bodily devotion boys my age were beginning to discover, realizing that attraction was something we would soon be powerless against, and gradually ridding themselves of the phobia, as a few of my friends already had, acting as though I were the strange one every time I made a comment about them spending their hallway time with some girl.

You want to sex me or what?

And even as I, too, was slowly handing my emotions over to attraction, letting my body guide me into a new phase that seemed to be occupying the minds and actions of my peers, Eddie and I were both males, and as males we had learned—if not from the older male cousins, then from the attitude that prevailed on the playground, the language, idioms, clothing, sports, perception, and familial expectations fed to us daily—that interacting with other males on a physical, intimate level was considered unacceptable, out of the question, a big no no, a reason why phrases such as *Boys should act like boys* existed, a step toward being viewed as gross, abnormal, toward having no friends. I became angrier in my embarrassment, afraid that Ricky and Eloy would see my aggression as something else, something we had all been taught to avoid. In that moment, at that age, there was no such thing as a broader perspective: there was only the dirt and heat and Eddie's words repeating in my head. I had no choice but to defend myself.

His nails were digging into my wrists, streaking a stigmata of scratches across my veins. I rotated my right wrist, slapped his hand away, and in two quick but awkward punches to the face—one to his cheek, the other to his jaw and neck—I ended our scuffle. Tears welled up in his eyes. His lips began to quiver. A rash-like redness pulsed through his tanned, sweat-beaded skin, and the expression on his face—caught between defeat, embarrassment, and general guilt for having provoked the situation further—was too much for me not to feel some immediate remorse in response, that and a sense of pity. He looked as though he were submerged underwater, in way too deep and out of breath. He looked like the child he was, and as I jumped off of him, got to my feet, still deciding whether or not to apologize at that moment or bask in the satisfaction that was building up inside of me for having put him in his place, the cries swelled in his throat, and the tears that had built up like the mucus from a stray dog's eyelids began to mix in with the smears of sweat seared across his face. If he were wearing eyeliner, I thought, he would have looked like my mother after a long night of arguing with my stepfather, the halos of sleeplessness ringed with that black, watercolor-like substance that was supposed to make her appearance younger, not exhausted. If his complexion had been lighter, the redness seeping through Eddie's pores would have looked like the blush on a circus clown's cheeks, and I would have perhaps felt more inclined to laugh.

Eddie zigzagged toward my grandmother's house, hands rubbing his face in an erratic attempt to relieve the pain my fists had created. He didn't look both ways before crossing the street. He didn't care. Ricky ran after him, while Eloy stopped next to me, saying something calm, slow, mindful of the situation, but which I immediately forgot, unsure if it would have served any purpose. I began to think of the consequences, what my mother would say, how she'd react to the berating remarks my aunt would confront her with: *Your son has anger issues, Maria Elena*; *If Eloy and Ricky hadn't stopped him, Eddie'd be in the hospital by now*; *It's always the quiet ones like Esteban that you have to watch out for, it's always the quiet ones*; *A sorry doesn't help, look at his face, look at his face, a sorry can't fix the bruises*. I'd imagine her semi-embellished concerns would continue, because what else could a mother do but defend her youngest son, think that there was no way in hell he could ever do something this wrong, that when we were out on the lot, it was I who instigated the situation, I who devirginized his ears with shit-talking, I who had no consideration for my cousin's feelings and thoughts, and I would should be chastised publicly, punished with a barrage of English and Spanish phrases, and maybe even a spanking, which I'm sure would make my aunt happy, or at least more at ease knowing that if Eddie did indeed play kickball with me again, or if we found ourselves on the verge of suddenly competing at a Sunday barbecue, I would keep my distance, having already learned what violence brings.

But then, as the thoughts of repercussions faded, and I could no longer imagine my aunt droning about her baby boy being hurt, I returned my attention to Eddie as he rounded the gate, shouted my grandmother's name, and opened the screen door, while Ricky slowed down, knowing he wasn't going to reach him in time to convince him to change the narrative, lessen the severity of what had just occurred.

My arms and legs grew numb. I felt exhausted, sleepy. How had I learned to punch like that? Had I watched too many *Rocky* films? Had I inherited, from all those evenings I eavesdropped on the commotion coming from my mother's room, my stepfather's sudden outbursts, his willingness to jam every word he knew back beneath his tongue and let the anger spreading in his body make the point his thoughts, his words, never could? Had I been mimicking my uncles too much, ditching, finally, my calmness and curiosity for a more direct approach, an outlet for my feelings that had immediate, visible, tangible results? Or was I simply becoming a combination of everyone I feared and loved, an inevitable product of my family, of our surroundings, and now, like a bird leaving the nest, inexpertly testing my strength against a world that, despite years of observation, I still knew little to nothing about.

I wanted to lie right there on the ground and forget not only what I had done, but also these dawning realizations: that I was someone who had the ability to change a body physically, to reshape skin and bone, to reshape the way another person thought about others, how they interacted with those they were sure they had every advantage over in this life. This—the power, the awareness of it—was me now, whether I wanted it to be or not.

Eddie disappeared inside the house. The door slammed. A small flock of sparrows, startled by the sudden noise, exploded from the strip of plants and flowers that made up my grandmother's garden, ascending like ceremonial ash into the sky before disappearing into the late afternoon bands of clouds that clustered like accomplices hiding, as best they could, the bruised and abandoned sun.

Acknowledgments

"After the Pyre" first appeared in *riverSedge*. My deepest gratitude to Charles McGregor and the staff at the journal.

Thank you to Lauren Westerfield for the care and insight provided throughout the editing process. This book would not be possible without your guidance.

Thank you to my mother, Maria Pérez, my sister, Iris Pérez, and my father, Pedro Espinoza, for the constant motivation and love.

Thank you to Norma Rodríguez, always and forever.

And thank you to Kristine Langley Mahler and everyone at the Split/Lip Press family for your faith in this book. With readers like you, anything is possible.

About the Author

Esteban Rodríguez is the author of the poetry collections *Dusk & Dust*, *Crash Course*, *In Bloom*, *(Dis)placement*, and *The Valley*. His poetry has appeared in *Boulevard*, *Shenandoah*, *The Rumpus*, *Tri-Quarterly*, and elsewhere. He is the Interviews Editor for the *Eco-Theo Review*, an Assistant Poetry Editor for *AGNI*, and a regular reviews contributor for *[PANK]* and *Heavy Feather Review*. He lives in Austin, Texas.

Now Available From

Split/Lip Press

For more info about the press and our titles, visit

www.splitlippress.com

Follow us on Twitter and Instagram: @splitlippress

Made in the USA
Monee, IL
12 January 2023

23483687R00079